RELEASE FROM SEXUAL TENSIONS

Release from Sexual Tensions

Toward an Understanding of Their Causes and Effects in Marriage

by Mary Steichen Calderone, M.D., M.S.P.H.

and Phyllis and Robert P. Goldman

Foreword by Robert W. Laidlaw, M.D.
Chief, Department of Psychiatry, Roosevelt Hospital, N.Y.C.
Past President, American Association of Marriage Counselors

Random House · New York

First Printing

Library of Congress Catalog Card Number: 60-5562

Manufactured in the United States of America

M.S.C. *to* F.A.C.

P.G. *and* R.P.G. *to each other*

FOREWORD

Few people—and this includes doctors—can talk about sex with ease and candor. Dr. Calderone is one of these rare people. The tone of this book is relaxed. It radiates warmth. It speaks simply and openly of matters which to many people are charged with high emotional tension. Only the most rigid of personalities could read this book without gaining a more understanding and accepting attitude toward sex.

The theme of the book might be epitomized in one simple statement: *Sex is good*—from the infant's first pleasurable awareness of his body down to the intimate love life of the elderly. It extends as well to the exploratory activities of the young child, the highly charged drive of the adolescent, and the increasingly varied experiences of the maturing years. Sex is good, subject to misuse, as with any other good thing, but remaining, in essence, good. It takes courage to sound this note in a society which, despite its many modern scientific advances, still carries along with it many deep emotional prejudices from the distant past.

To the clinical psychiatrist and to the marriage counselor this book will be of unique value for use with patients. Psychiatry, despite its many differing schools of thought, is coming more and more to recognize one central therapeutic tool—the healing power of love. Too often in our patients' minds, sex and love are placed at opposite poles. This book brings them together.

For those who are in conflict in regard to past sexual experiences, this book will offer comfort and hope; for young people who are searching for guidance in their own future development, it provides wise counsel.

ROBERT W. LAIDLAW, M.D.
Chief, Psychiatric Service, Roosevelt Hospital, New York City
Past President, American Association of Marriage Counselors, Inc.

December 22, 1959

CONTENTS

Contents

Contents

INTRODUCTION

A while ago, I mentioned casually to some young friends that I was writing a book about sexual tensions in married life. The wife smiled wryly. "Do you want to hear about ours?" she asked half jokingly. "We've had our share. . . ."

I asked then, and I do now, "But who hasn't?"

I do not know of a husband or wife who has not at some time or other experienced profound tensions concerning sexuality. Virtually universal are fears, self-doubts, illusions and any number of anxieties concerning sex in marriage. In a sense, such emotional reactions to this sacred and beautiful undertaking are inevitable. So much is at stake. So much needs to be learned, and perhaps unlearned.

The questions that arise again and again in the minds of couples are well known to almost everyone. Will our sexual union be successful, rewarding, pleasurable? Or will we fail? Will it hurt, physically or emotionally? Will our sex life grow in meaning and importance through the years? Or will it wane after a brief, intense period? And if it wanes—what then?

These are but a few of the questions that are silently and universally asked against a background of never-ending complexities. In this background are the individual's upbringing, the climate of his own home, a lifetime of experience as infant, child, adolescent, "dater" and, finally, as husband or wife. In addition, of course, there is the world we live in today, with its changing rules and standards—or lack of them—and its strong pressures.

All the components of one's upbringing and past fuse to create the attitudes, beliefs and values that one brings to marriage. The husband and wife are conditioned by what they have been told, or have not been told, seen or not seen, experienced or not experienced; by their attitudes toward themselves; and by the fictions and facts superimposed by our American culture.

In our society, we are confronted very often by what seem to be dreadful paradoxes about sex. On the one hand, sex is represented as "dirty," base, animal-like and degrading. On the other, it is pictured as an ultimate expression of the individual, a source of joy and self-realization which cannot truly be described, hard as authors try. Still again, it is pictured as rosy, sentimental, sweet, or with a certain magical, unreal quality, or mystical and spiritual and far removed from earthly things.

Somewhere between such representations of sexuality there is a great area of unknowing for countless couples who rely on hearsay, chance and guesswork in their sexual lives. Lacking information and insight, they flounder. If they achieve full sexual gratification and growth through the married years, it is often pure luck. They may never have stopped to consider what they could do to emerge from the vacuum of their ignorance—an ignorance not only of facts but of feelings.

This state of affairs, this tragic vacuum, may persist for a short time in marriage, for years, or for the duration of the marriage itself. Unhappily, many couples are affected. It is for these countless married couples plagued by tensions, fears, doubt and disappointment in their sex lives that this book is written. It is written, too, for the couples who have all but given up, and who look upon sex passively, as if it hardly existed. I hope, too, that young people recently married and those about to be married will find something here for them. This book is for all ages. Most will find in it things that did apply once, may apply now, or will surely apply later.

This book is not written for the emotionally disturbed husband or wife urgently in need of psychiatric care, to whom sex may be a terrible and forbidding ritual. Nor is it written for those couples who have achieved a sustained and satisfying sex life together. No, this is for those in the great middle group who open-mindedly seek ways to make sex the great and constructive force in their lives that it could and should be.

Sufficient maturity and understanding to welcome sex as a positive force can place you squarely on the road to happiness in marriage. For most this is not easy, and cannot be achieved in an instant. The thoughts in this book may perhaps stand as guideposts for you along the way.

—Mary Steichen Calderone, M.D.

Great Neck, New York
1959

RELEASE FROM SEXUAL TENSIONS

I

Learning, Unlearning, Relearning

From the vital standpoint of marital love, you may feel that you have not yet begun to live. Or you may feel that you have stopped living. Neither of these need be true.

Once, when I was a little girl in France, I met a kind old priest in a railway carriage. He asked me, "What is the most beautiful age to be, my child?"

All during that hour's trip I guessed first one age and then another, never the right one. Just as we drew to our final stop, he smiled sweetly at me and said, "The age you are now, my child, the age you are now, and the age you will be every day of your life."

What a tender thought. Yes, and how wonderfully true, if

we can only allow ourselves to see it that way. Instead, many of us deprive ourselves of the beauties of every age because of feelings that somehow encroach: fear, hate, distrust, ignorance, suspicion; and *wanting to win at all costs.*

Unfortunately, these are the feelings that we allow, all too often, to become associated with sex. They are the feelings which can make us unable to achieve sexual fulfillment, and that can create great tensions concerning what should be a vital part of marital living.

In succeeding chapters, we shall explore prevalent causes of sexual tensions, with some case histories. In addition, we shall attempt to provide guideposts, specific and general, as to how such tensions can be overcome, or better still, avoided. We shall analyze important forces in everyday living which threaten sexual adjustment, and still others which enhance it.

Sex Fears and Ignorance

The many cases of fear, lack of knowledge, immaturity and failure relating to marital sex find expression in a wide range of ways. An individual's habits, a chance remark, a touch, failure to show simple consideration—these and a host of other commonplace factors can cause sexual tensions over short and long periods. Many of these are resolved with time. Some are not, until the husband and wife make a conscious effort to do so. Still others require outside help. There is no pat formula, no set of blueprints that will apply to every case, for this is an extraordinarily complex subject, a sensitive one that simply cannot be dealt with in sweeping, all-encompassing fashion.

Let us explore how ignorance might affect couples. The first history represents an extreme case. The others are more commonplace.

A couple in their late thirties consulted a physician, complaining that they were childless.

"I assume that you have intercourse regularly," the doctor said inquiringly.

"Oh, yes," the husband replied. "We've been married fourteen years and we have had intercourse at least a dozen times."

The doctor could hardly believe his ears and pressed further for information. He learned that both husband and wife had assumed at marriage that the first time they had intercourse, the wife would become pregnant. This did not happen.

Husband and wife had been brought up to consider sex as sinful and consequently they looked upon sex play prior to intercourse as distasteful. They not only waited a full year before indulging once again in intercourse, but the husband revealed, after much additional questioning, that he had never achieved orgasm. Yet, amazingly, this couple in all seriousness came to the doctor's office to ask why they had failed to conceive.

Or consider the case of a twenty-eight-year-old housewife and her thirty-year-old husband. She told her doctor the following story:

"We have been married seven years and have seven children. I have asked my husband if he or I could use something when we're having intercourse to prevent my getting pregnant.

"He told me that the things we might use are harmful and will decrease his satisfaction—so we've just never tried them. Isn't there *anything* we can do to stop having babies?"

Once again, ignorance and misinformation had resulted in great and unnecessary distress—for nine people this time.

Or perhaps more typical is the case of the newly married couple whose marriage was endangered on the wedding night. Intercourse on that first night broke the wife's hymen and she bled slightly. Not knowing that this is comparatively common, the wife became frightened, thinking that something must be wrong with her sexual organs.

For months, she avoided her husband. On those rare occasions when they had intercourse, she did not bleed, of course, but she feared she might. An explanation from her doctor set her mind at ease; but in her case lack of information once again had caused needless tension and fear, and delay in establishing a good marital relationship.

I cite these cases simply to illustrate that such things do go on in the twentieth-century atomic age. Such cases, and they are not few, represent one end of the spectrum of marital failure. On the other end, there are cases of real cruelty such as the following:

A young couple in their thirties discussed quite openly with their physician the wife's habit of using sex as a form of punishment or reward. When the husband displeased her, she would simply refuse intercourse, and would taunt him about it. When the husband won her favor, perhaps with some small, considerate act or with a gift, she consented to intercourse.

"I realize," the husband said, "that my wife uses sex as a weapon in our marriage. For a while, I tried to fight it. I tried to reason with her. But now, I just don't care. I'm tired of hitting my head against a wall."

Significantly, the husband is becoming a heavy drinker. He regards his wife coolly, with a certain detachment. They have two children and I suspect that the entire family is extremely unhappy, for the friction generated between husband and wife inevitably affects the children, and the youngsters are well aware that they are living in an unhappy home.

This case is a typical example of marital sexual tension. It illustrates how strong, ill-founded emotions can displace what should be the dominant tone of marriage, namely, a genuine concern for the welfare of the partner with a desire for "oneness," for an all-pervasive affection and for personality growth through living together.

What can we do to reverse the flow of misinformation, fear and negative emotions?

I believe that we must work toward understanding ourselves

if we are to help ourselves gain release from sexual tensions. In the end that is what we must do, *help ourselves.* Of course we can blame our parents for what they did or did not do in regard to teaching us about sex. Indeed, our children may blame us. However, that is too easy, too pat. You can set up a scapegoat, but does that really help? I think not. We must go deeper than that and try to understand what went wrong and how it can be made right again.

Sex Education—Unplanned

Most parents believe they have fulfilled their responsibilities to their children if they explain how the baby grows in the mother, how the baby is born, and even, hardest of all, how the baby got into the mother in the first place. Parents often fail to realize that this is only a tiny part of sex education, and is hardly sufficient as a basis for a healthy outlook on sex in later adulthood.

Actually, the greatest part of sex education is unplanned by the parents. It begins very soon after the baby is born, when he first becomes aware of the difference in how he is handled by his mother and by his father, the difference in their voices, their body odors, the feel of their skin and muscles next to his. As he grows older, he begins to notice how his own body is made and, later on, how other people's bodies are made.

As time goes on in his childhood, he absorbs, without even realizing it, various "feeling tones" about sex. These are transmitted in a great many ways by the people closest to him, his parents. The mother's and father's conversations, touches, glances, all play a part. Their feelings about each other as reflected in their actions, attitudes and tone of voice toward each other also take on great importance.

At some time, the small child senses his mother's attitude

toward herself and toward her own body. The same holds true for the child's realizations about his father, and about both his parents' feelings toward each other. (As you would expect, an overall climate in the home of love, awareness, consideration and warmth becomes transferred to the child.) Similarly, intelligent, secure, comfortable attitudes toward sex are transferred to the youngster.

All of these might be called "inward feelings." Also vital to the child's early sexual education are the "outward feelings," that is, how the parents see themselves and act in relation to their community, to other men and other women and to society as a whole. Gradually, the child becomes aware in this area, too, even though the parents may not realize it. The awareness grows as if the child had sensitive antennae reaching out to record parental emotions and actions in his own mind—for future use or for future rejection.

The Unspoken Words

Few parents realize that their body movements in the normal daily routine, their glances, their actions without words, represent strong ways of speaking. This is called "nonverbal communication" and children are extremely sensitive to it.

I shall never forget a discussion some friends of mine once had concerning a mutual acquaintance. One man in the group was discussing the acquaintance's abilities as a household mechanic. A second man in the group merely shrugged his shoulders, but in the shrug you could see that he was really disparaging the person under discussion. At that moment, his three-and-a-half-year-old child looked at him inquiringly and said, "Why don't you like Charlie? Don't you think he's any good?"

Not a word had been spoken criticizing Charlie, but this is how nonverbal communication works. As it applies to a youngster's early sex education and his overall feelings about sex, this form of communication carries great weight. Indeed, actions can speak louder than words in almost every phase of living.

Supposing the parents' verbal and nonverbal communication concerning their relationship, sex and the nature of living itself are essentially healthy, straightforward and honest? Then, as I have said, the child is likely to grow up with similar attitudes and emotions. But supposing the climate of the home is basically unhealthy?

Maladjusted Parents

Let's assume that the mother resents her status. She feels trapped and unappreciated in the household. Further, she may believe that her husband is an inadequate provider, that she could have pursued a career more successfully than he. Suppose that, hating her own role as a wife and mother, she feels she has to compete in the home to prove her superiority. These emotions, or shades of them in one direction or another, are fairly common.

Now let's proceed a step further. With such an aggressive, unhappy wife, the husband may feel that his masculinity is threatened. Perhaps he wasn't altogether sure of his masculinity in the first place. In this situation, he might react in one of two ways. He might fight back in an attempt to prove how strong, aggressive and masculine he really is. Or, he might accept his wife's analysis of the situation, believe it and turn into a submerged Mr. Milquetoast. This, too, is a common state of affairs.

The point is this: the two types of relationships in marriage I have just described make for two quite different kinds of home. The children growing up in these two homes would absorb distinctly different attitudes and beliefs about the roles of men and women in marriage. Their concepts of the relationship of the sexes would be radically different.

Yet, this would result without any instruction at all or discussion of how babies were born, the nature of intercourse, masturbation, frigidity or any other concepts associated with sexual behavior. Obviously, then, the climate of the home sets the stage for the child's attitudes on sex, and this climate adds up to very powerful sex education indeed.

I know a young woman, an only child, who was brought up by her mother to believe that sexual play and intercourse, even in marriage, were "dirty." Proper wives, her mother conditioned her to believe, avoided intercourse as much as possible because, she said, it was basically degrading.

The young woman grew up and married. Interestingly, she sought out a rather mild, meek, passive man. I am convinced that she selected this type of man because she felt, consciously or unconsciously, that she could dominate him in all phases of their marriage, including the sexual one.

Tragically, history did repeat itself in this case. The young woman had only one child, a daughter, to whom she passed on the same unwholesome emotions about sex. The third generation marriage has been just as unhappy as the first and second generation marriages were; all three are almost carbon copies of each other.

Sex Education Outside the Home

Of course, sex education is found also in a wide variety of places outside the home. In almost every experience a small child has, there is some sexual component, in that the child receives some idea of sex differences, both behavioral and physical, between boys and girls, men and women. In school, visiting friends and relatives, at the movies, at play, there is inevitably some sex education, direct or indirect, obvious or hidden, deriving from the child's own observation of other people's feelings and attitudes about sex.

Sex and Our "Romantic" Tradition

Still another major factor in the sex education of the youngster is our overemphasis on the romantic aspect of sexual behavior. No other country in the world provides its young people with such a lopsided view of marriage, symbolized by the Hollywood movie, the television dramatic show and the romance magazine article. Courtship in this romantic tradition is pretty much sugar-coated. Rarely is dating recognized as a period of real upheaval, when teen-agers inevitably come to ask themselves, "How far should I go?" "Am I doing right by allowing a boy to touch me?" "Why, if I am as mature physically as an adult, shouldn't I have adult sexual experiences?"

Actually, the beautiful kiss of courtship is not an end in itself, but rather a beginning. It symbolizes a pact in which two people make a decision to live together. People who expect their relationship to remain at the level of the romantic courtship kiss are bound to be terribly disappointed. Life simply is not like that. Marital sex, beautiful as it can be, progressively unfolding in richness through the years, simply does not exist on the pink-cotton-candy level of courtship.

Only if you are mature enough and sufficiently full of eagerness to live, to learn and to compromise, will you reap the rewards of sexual fulfillment in marriage. You will see the symbolic courtship kiss as the starting point for a great experience of give and take—sometimes more on one side, sometimes more on the other.

Goals of Marriage

You will see marriage as an exciting adventure of progressive discovery, of yourself as well as of your mate. You will know the boundless, ecstatic joy of having your husband or your wife become more important to you than anybody else in the world; more important than you are to yourself. You will reap the rewards of companionship in all sorts of ways, the fun of having an understanding husband or wife to laugh with joyously, to laugh at tenderly, to share the lasting joys as well as the deep sorrows with. You will come to know the supreme comfort of having someone to whom you really belong, of having a home base that is always there for you and for you alone; the sense of privilege when you are sure that your spouse looks upon you as his home base.

Certainly even in the happy marriage there are fights, disagreements and arguments. There may even be some rather full-scale battles. But in the basically happy marriage, these serve merely to adjust one mate to the other. The disputes never really threaten the security of the relationship. In fact, this kind of tension, where partners care enough about each other to be aware of areas of disagreement needing adjustment, may make a more alive kind of marriage than one where the partners are not aware and care less.

Compromise and Learning in Sex

Inevitably, too, in this type of happy marriage, there is a tremendous give and take in the sexual relationship. Almost certainly there are tensions, failures, astounding successes and new discoveries—even after many years of experience. Implicit in the sexuality of marriage is trial and error, success and failure. Only the immature believe that "it begins wonderfully and never changes," or that "if it isn't wonderful now it never can be," or that "tonight's failure ruins everything forever."

Implicit, too, in the healthy sex of marriage is a certain amount of crudeness mixed with tenderness, a certain amount of experimentation mixed with accomplishment. Later, there are the rugged dislocations brought by the coming of children. But then, far outweighing the dislocation is the shared sense of achievement when the rough spots are smoothed into a new area of growth.

These are some of the reasons why the marriage relationship, a man and woman living together because they want to live together, is the most precious and deeply satisfying relationship that we know. In some ways, it is even more important than the relationship between parent and child, for it is *the* basic and fundamental relationship of life, and if it is a sound one, then the parent-child relationship will almost surely be equally sound.

I have stated that there are a good many forces at work in our homes and in our culture that multiply sexual tensions in marriage. Early conditioning, unfounded fears, lack of information, courtship customs and the romantic tradition are among the leading factors.

For the married couple today, little is achieved by blaming their parents for the attitudes and emotions brought to marital sex. A certain amount of unhealthy thinking and feeling is inevitably brought to most marriages. It is up to the couples themselves to counteract and reverse such beliefs. In short, most married couples today must try to work out by and for themselves the solutions to their sexual tensions. But how?

Sexual Adjustment—from Within Ourselves

The key lies within each one of us, where there already exist all the necessary ingredients for sexual happiness and fulfillment. Part of the answer lies in understanding our own attitudes and knowledge; part of the answer, too, involves our own capacity and desire to change.

Patience, too, is a vital factor, as are gentleness, sympathetic understanding and love that is not bounded only by sexuality, but by respect, trust and admiration as well.

Finally, once a couple has attained the knowledge, understanding and desire to do something positive about sexuality, the final hurdle involves action itself. You must do something positive. You must set your course toward freedom from guilt, from suspicion, from recrimination. Too often, we forget that sex and guilt need not be synonymous. Sexuality, after all, is a normal, vital function which should not engender guilt. Indeed, too few of us permit ourselves to regard sex partly as fun. Yet, if you are mature enough to recognize the real value of sex in marriage, you must also recognize, openly and without innuendo, that sex can be light-hearted, gay, occasionally funny, and full of laughter.

Thus, to re-emphasize what we said earlier, the key to release from sexual tensions is to *face your own feelings* about sex.

Your Life Is Like a Movie Film

In this book, we are going to pretend that your early life, experiences and teachings are on a movie film, and that you now have a chance to review that film, to rewind it and rerun it several times over.

Be the Editor of Your Life Film

Rerun, as it were, that film of your long and intricate sex education and sex experiences. When you review it—and you can, if you are honest and sincere and patient with yourself—you may be able to achieve a kind of wonderful erasure of past mistakes, and in place of them, you may be able to substitute healthy attitudes and emotions concerning sex in marriage. That is the real purpose of this book—to help you do just that.

2

The Years from Twelve to Eighteen

I am writing this chapter for two purposes. First, I want to present important ideas that will help newly married and young married couples to look back and understand the teen years through which they have just passed. This will make it easier for them to rerun their memory film and to re-edit it in the light of their present understanding of how things are and how they got that way. Second, I think it is important that teen-agers who are engaged now or are contemplating marriage (and even those who are not) understand certain facts about sex—and I am not only talking about how babies are born.

I must admit, though, that in writing for or about the teen years, I know the odds are against me. In all probability, those young people who do not need this chapter will read it, and those who need it most will not.

Importance of the Teen Years

The years from twelve to eighteen are just about the most important in your lives. Up to the age of twelve, you have had very little to do with your own development. After the age of twelve, *you* play the biggest role in turning yourself into the kind of person you will be most of the rest of your life.

In these five or six years, you begin making up your mind about things—or not making it up. This is when you begin crystallizing your attitudes and feelings. With these attitudes and feelings, you will be making some of the most important decisions you can ever make: how and where you earn your living; and how and whom you marry. Whether or not we like to admit it, it is our attitudes and feelings that govern us in these all-important decisions; not our minds, not our intellects. If we are honest, we will recognize that even when our minds tell us one thing, our attitudes and feelings can fool us into believing that just the opposite is better.

How You Are Vulnerable

This is a very vulnerable period in your life. By "vulnerable" I mean that you are particularly liable to betray yourself into doing exactly the opposite from what you had intended to do. Here are four ways in which this can happen:

(1) You discover how pleasant—and how essential—it is to be part of a gang or a specific group. However, to be part of it, you must be like it, not different from it. How do you pick the gang that you will be part of? Do you stand off and make a

careful survey of all the gangs available to you? Do you even know how many different kinds of gangs and different kinds of activities there are?

No such luck, for most young people. The gang that is handy is the gang you join—if it will have you. If it is the kind of gang that doesn't believe in all the things you believe in, you can always kid yourself into believing that you were wrong in the first place and that what the gang wants is what you had wanted all the time. *You are vulnerable to the need to belong to a gang and you may be betrayed by this need into choosing one that is wrong for the kind of person you really are.*

(2) In the years from twelve to eighteen, you become independent of your parents, your family, your teachers. This assertion of your independence is normal and imperative, but it can be so imperative that you may make the wrong decisions just to show that you *are* independent. *You are vulnerable to this need to assert your independence and you can be betrayed by it when it pushes you into making decisions and choices that you actually don't believe in.*

(3) This is a time for asserting independence, but it may also be a time of just drifting along. Sometimes, making decisions or developing positive attitudes is too difficult or too uncomfortable. It can be much easier to float along, meeting each situation as it comes and sometimes, even then, ducking the issue. *You are vulnerable to this natural tendency to let things slide and take care of themselves. You can be betrayed by it when you get caught in a critical situation that you can't get out of because you have developed no effective convictions and attitudes on which you can rely in a jam.*

(4) In this age you are Youth itself. It is marvelous and glorious. We know this is so because everyone who ever lived has been marvelously and gloriously young at one time. *But, you are vulnerable because the very fact that you are young makes you believe that it is a sign of weakness and lack of character to*

accept guidance from any older person. You can be betrayed by this belief into cutting off your nose to spite your face.

Sex Knowledge

I suppose sex is the most critical area in the teen years for which decisions and attitudes have to be shaped. You probably know a lot or at least something about it now, but you will know a great deal more by the time you are fifty. You will wish then that some of the things you know could have been applied at the age you are now.

You should make it your business to obtain as many straight facts about sex as possible. There is no excuse in this day for any young person not to have accurate information about it. There are books in school and public libraries, and there are good and competent people everywhere ready to share their knowledge with you. To rely for information on the next fellow, who talks and thinks the most about sex and considers himself an authority, is stupid and lazy, for it lays you open to all kinds of misinformation and unhealthy attitudes. Among the grown people you know—your doctor, your minister, your teacher, your Scout leaders—there must be at least one you can trust to talk to about sex. Getting this information is the least you owe yourself.

However, even the best teachers may lead you to believe that sex begins and ends with the sex act itself. Factual information about sex is essential—but what good are facts if your feelings about those facts are twisted? Furthermore, books that can give you knowledge about sex never tell you what sex really is.

Sex is:
exciting and wonderful;
the basic human relationship;
essential to life as a whole;

an experience that, under the right circumstances, will grow and improve with age. To make it grow takes a good deal of effort on the part of *two* married people.

an experience that, under the wrong circumstances, can go sour on you; this takes hardly any effort at all.

And books and teachers never tell you what sex is not.

Sex is not:
necessary for health;
the only thing in life;
the only thing in marriage;
the same thing as love.

The Place of Sex in Life

Because sex is uppermost in the minds of most people, it becomes extremely important for you to determine just what place it is going to occupy in your life. For instance,

Sex can:
be the dominating interest in your life;
determine who your friends are;
determine whom you marry;
determine when you marry;
determine whether you marry at all.

That is, sex can do these things if *you* are not the boss but allow it to boss you.

How Sex Is "Used"

Sex often is "used" by people in ways that do not have much bearing on its original purposes. For instance,

Sex is used:

to prove something—maleness, femaleness, your importance, your independence of your parents, what have you;
to conquer someone—or anyone;
to give vent to feelings of hate, revenge, frustration;
to obtain comfort in times of anxiety and stress.

When sex is used in these ways the partner is not a true partner, but is merely a convenience—a device, as it were.

When sex is used—or shall I say misused—in these ways, often it can boomerang. For instance, after a while, no more kicks; it all gets to be pretty much the same thing. Then what? Then you may end up by proving just the opposite of what you intended to prove by your "use" or rather misuse of sex.

Also, when you use sex to express what it was never intended to express, for instance if you use it as a weapon, then it may eventually desert you completely. This is known as impotence or frigidity.

Then how *is* sex really intended to be used? The answer to that question must be arrived at by each individual for himself—just as each person must eventually answer for himself the question, How do we know there is a God?

By and large, the most knowledgeable people believe that the two great and essential purposes of sex are: to express love for a partner who has true meaning for you in your life *outside* of sex; and to create children for whom you and your partner intend to be parents in the full sense of the word.

To use sex in these two ways requires two devoted partners who *both* participate not only in the act itself, but in the decisions *for* the act and in the meaning *of* the act.

You Were Born Rich

When you are making important decisions and developing important attitudes you start with three riches as a base. You were born endowed with these three things, true, but only with their beginnings. How each one develops is up to you. These are the three riches each person is born with:

A body—you will live inside it until the day you die. If *you* are too lazy to take care of it, who else will?

A mind—to think with, plan with, decide with, do things with. If *you* are too lazy to use it in these ways, who else can?

A personality—to feel with, to express feelings with, to find meanings with. This is like a bank account. If you fail to make deposits or if you make bad investments, there is no interest, and you end up poor or bankrupt at fifty—or maybe even younger.

Believe It—or Not

I don't expect any young person reading this to believe all or any of it. As a matter of fact, I didn't at their age; so I had to learn it all the hard way, as did most people alive today, and as perhaps you will too. But for this pigheadedness I and a great many others paid a big price, because one always pays a price for pigheadedness; and the prices being paid today are measured in:

divorces,
cases of gonorrhea and syphilis,
suicides,
alcoholism,
mental breakdowns,
inability to hold jobs,
crimes of violence,
drug addiction,
babies born to unmarried girls and women of all ages from twelve up, and
just plain sorrow and bitterness.

Many people are paying these high, high prices—people just like yourself. At some key point in their lives they could have made a decision for or against something, but either they made the wrong decision, or they didn't make any decision at all but just floated along with the tide. They chose the quicker and easier rather than the longer and more difficult way.

In the next few years, moments of decision will be coming thick and fast at you. Will you field them, or fumble them?

Twenty years from now, you will know the answer.

3

Common Causes of Sexual Tensions

Many Couples Lack Information About Their Bodies

It seems difficult to believe, yet a significant number of couples simply do not have the fundamental information about their own sexual organs or their mate's. Often, the lack of information is startling. Recently, a patient said to his doctor: "Now that my wife has had a hysterectomy, I guess we can never have sexual intercourse again. Isn't that right, Doctor?"

Of course, it's not right; it's dead wrong, for the operation involves removal of the uterus, nothing more. It is shocking that the husband was totally unaware of what was involved in the operation and of the fact that it had no relation to his or his wife's future capacity for sex.

His is only one case. A physician friend tells of a patient, a man of thirty-one, who actually asked what was involved in menstruation and why his wife preferred not to have intercourse during her monthly period. (The doctor explained, of course, that most women abstain during their menstrual period for esthetic or perhaps hygienic reasons, or because of real or imagined discomfort.) Again, it seems difficult to believe, but such things happen. They are not exceptional but common. Ignorance of basic bodily functions is widespread.

Such lack of information can be overcome, of course, by reading a sound, authoritative book on the subject; by consulting a marriage counselor, physician or minister; or by taking a marriage preparation course at the YMCA, YWCA, Planned Parenthood Center or any other of the increasingly numerous resources for such courses in our larger cities.

Husband and Wife Don't Really Talk to Each Other

One of the most tragic causes of sexual disappointment stems from a single fact: husbands and wives are frequently unable to discuss their mutual problem with each other. How shortsighted! If you cannot turn to your spouse for help in this most intimate matter, to whom can you turn? Fear, pride, timidity—all these and more prevent sensible husband-wife communication on the subject of sex. Yet, the couple should stop to think about what actually might be gained by talking it out.

I have been told by many couples that "sex is a subject we simply do not discuss, even between ourselves." This is a strikingly immature attitude. It says, in effect, that my spouse, the person whom I have selected to live with for life, the person who will help raise our children, may somehow fail to understand or be sympathetic toward my feelings on a subject of critical importance to both of us.

It may also indicate that the husband or wife is afraid to face the issue, afraid to articulate it, afraid that he or she will lose face. Frank, candid and honest evaluation between husband and wife of any critical problem in marriage is essential if the marriage is to develop in love and stability.

Some Are Ashamed

Shame and guilt are two tones of emotion which, like fear, can cause sexual tensions. They are, unfortunately, extremely common. Frequently, they stem from childhood, but they may arise from the courtship or the marriage itself. Most often these commonplace barriers to complete marital sex fulfillment can be removed wholly or in significant part by the couple themselves, or by intelligent counseling from a doctor, minister or marriage expert.

Very often, the antidote to shame lies within us if we are willing to admit the shame in the first place. Very often, shame can be dissolved by honesty, understanding and patience.

I recall a young woman in her early twenties who couldn't bear to undress in front of her husband just after they were married. This is a more common problem than you may think. At first the husband was offended, but soon he began to realize the sincerity of his wife's feelings.

The couple solved the problem by turning out the lights in their bedroom before retiring. Gradually, the wife became able to accept undressing together in the unlighted room. In a short time, husband and wife agreed to leave one dim light on. Today, three years later, she feels no shame in undressing in their fully lighted bedroom, and their sexual life together has become increasingly satisfying.

Let's Not Forget Fatigue

In our hectic way of life, fatigue—emotional or physical or both—is a major cause of sexual incompleteness. Either the husband is dog-tired because of his work load, or the wife may be exhausted by her chores and care of the children. Either he or she may resist even sex play and manual stimulation toward climax.

Such refusals are bound to cause tensions, because they are inevitably ill-timed from the standpoint of the other partner. Here is when compromise comes into the picture. At times, the tired husband or wife would be well advised to participate in sexual activity, knowing that maximum effort cannot be expended or enjoyment achieved, but motivated by the wish to give joy to the other. Thus, couples can decrease tensions by giving in, now and again, to the desires of each other as we have just seen in a case history. Certainly concessions should not set the complete tone of the marriage, but if the partners concede to each other *sometimes,* they stand a far greater chance of reaching rapport *most of the time.*

Changing Moods Can Affect Sex

If husband or wife is depressed, worried or preoccupied with some problem, sex may seem unattractive. All of us experience peaks and troughs in our moods. These are normal in everyday living.

Before a husband or wife becomes angry because the other is moody, it should be remembered that the overwhelming majority of such mood variations are temporary. They are what doctors call "self-limiting." They come, but more important, they go. When they do, sexuality should once again assume its true importance. Of course, a depression that persists may require medical attention, but most depressions are temporary. We simply snap out of them.

However, the point is that when emotional factors affect sexuality, large amounts of patience, warmth, tolerance and tenderness are called for. Forcing the issue may simply worsen the situation.

I know a couple who found themselves brooding about their sexual life because the husband was sometimes moody. His moods seemed to sap his energy and he simply did not want coitus. Over a period of weeks, his wife drew out the cause of his tension.

"He felt he would never amount to anything in his company," the wife related. "Here he was making a good living, but he felt frozen in his job. We had a series of long talks. Finally, I persuaded him to consult his boss concerning his future."

The husband put his cards on the table with his immediate superior and was informed that the company valued greatly the job he was doing. His future was assured. Thus, the husband realized that his job anxiety had no real basis in fact. This anxiety dissolved, he could once again return to normal living, which, of course, included full sexual activity.

When the husband or wife goes into an emotional tailspin, the first task is to cope with the emotional problem. Once that is resolved, the marriage will usually resume its natural course.

"But we haven't the room . . ."

Among a great many couples there may be intense sexual tension because their homes seem inadequate. Thus, a small child may have to sleep in the same room with the parents. They, on the other hand, know full well that the normal sounds of intercourse may wake the child or cause fear or an unhealthy reaction in him. This, of course, inhibits the free play of marital sex.

What to do? I can only recommend that small children never be allowed to sleep in the same room with their parents, even if there is a partition or room divider. The parents' privacy is invaded, and so is that of the infant. Any makeshift possible should be employed to avoid this situation.

I know of many a marriage in which the only bedroom in the apartment has been relinquished to the child. The parents then sleep in the living room or in a dining area. This may sound uncomfortable to some, but it assures peace of mind for the parents.

It is difficult to tell at what age an infant, who accidentally sees or hears his parents during intercourse, will be "scarred" emotionally. This is a point still argued by experts. Although they may not agree on the age, all agree on the inevitable bad effects of a child's sharing his parents' bedroom after two years of age. And from the parents' point of view, there is sure to be a good deal of tension that is better avoided.

The Fear of Inadequate Performance

Certainly one of the major tension-causing factors in marriage is fear on the part of one partner or the other that sexual relations will not be satisfying to either or both. Let me hasten to say that this fear is extremely common. It is felt at one time or another by most couples.

Of course, the male reaches climax more easily, so he is less likely to be inhibited by this fear. However, if he reaches climax before his wife, his anxiety may stem from a belief that he is not an adequate sex partner for his wife.

The cases of premature ejaculation among men are so common, especially at the beginning of marriage, that they can be considered more or less normal. However, as intercourse is practiced more frequently, this fear of inadequate performance tapers off considerably. Also, men themselves learn little ways to stave off climax so that their wives may "catch up to them" in coitus. Men learn to pace themselves, to slow down when they feel climax imminent, to assume one or another position in which timing will be more compatible.

It is important to remember in this connection that women do not always reach climax, nor do they always seek to. Recent studies show rather conclusively that one third of all wives reach climax much of the time, one third some of the time, and the final one third rarely if ever. This, of course, is in sharp contrast to the male, who is likely to experience climax most of the time.

The point is this: Almost every young married couple experiences fear of inadequate performance; time usually diminishes this fear *if* couples will simply give each other a chance—a chance to experiment, to fail, to succeed and to learn.

One husband I know was plagued by anxieties concerning his sexual capabilities. He always experienced climax before his wife could do so. The husband actually told his wife, "I guess I'm not much when it comes to stimulating you sexually." He was discouraged and downhearted.

His wife, a loving, calm, sympathetic person, decided on a course of action. "I decided," she says, "to apply an old idea, suggestion. So when we went to bed, I reassured my husband gently that in my eyes he was a really virile person and in time this would be revealed."

After some months the results of her gentle persuasion and suggestion were obvious to both. Gradually, the husband began to feel that he really was sexually competent. As the belief became strengthened, his entire attitude on sex changed, and he was able to hold himself in check until his wife could achieve her climax.

That was five years ago. The couple now has three children.

Their sexual life is harmonious; both the husband and wife have become mature people who love and respect each other completely.

The Fear of Pregnancy

I shall never forget a letter in which a young wife and mother said: "We've been married five years next month and have four children. I'm afraid that I'm pregnant once again. I'm still young, but I feel old. I'm terrified. What can I do?"

Obviously, that couple had never known of simple contraceptive measures, or if they had known, they had not employed such measures, even though their religion would have encouraged them to do so. There are a great many couples like them, whose failure to seek out the facts about contraception compounds their tensions. In this enlightened day, such inaction is inexcusable. If the couple is Catholic, then the "rhythm method" should be learned, preferably from a doctor especially skilled in the method. Medical contraceptive techniques have proved more than 95 percent effective. The rhythm method is more than 80 percent effective among women who have very regular menstrual periods. Among others, rhythm is far less effective.

It is important to remember one point. Some couples practice a form of contraception known as coitus interruptus, in which the male withdraws his penis just prior to climax. This is not a wise way to achieve contraception. It is rarely fulfilling either to the husband or wife. It can actually distort sexual habits in such a fashion that sex becomes distasteful to both parties concerned.

Fear of pregnancy takes on special aspects immediately after the first child is born. First, the wife is likely to shun intercourse because of the possibility of an early second pregnancy. Then, too, she has been so busy with the baby all day long that she is too tired to want intercourse.

Her feelings must be contrasted with those of the husband. For the last two months or so of the pregnancy, intercourse was forbidden by the doctor, and also for several weeks after the new mother and baby returned from the hospital. Thus, the male may feel unfulfilled while his wife may be anxiety-ridden and exhausted. Here, many factors can ease the situation. First, there should be a certain amount of discussion about mutual feelings. Then, contraceptive advice should be sought from the doctor. Finally, in this trying "post-baby period," just as in the prenatal months, the husband may accept manual stimulation leading to orgasm from a wife who he knows will later be ready to return to full sexual relations.

"My mind is on other things . . ."

At times, a husband or wife may be so preoccupied with other interests that sex takes a back seat. I suspect that in this competitive society of ours, it is the husband who becomes preoccupied with his particular strivings more often than the wife.

A young wife told me how this affected her marriage for a time.

"There was a period about two years ago when my husband was driving himself hard down at his office. He felt he was at a turning point in his career. He got a sudden and feverish surge of energy at work, feeling that he must make his mark then or never.

"I wanted a child desperately at the time. But every night when he came home, he said he was too tired to have intercourse.

"At first I was furious. I began shouting at him for the least little thing. In a few weeks, I began to realize that my attitude not only produced hostility in me and guilt in him, but it was endangering the marriage itself.

"One day, I simply resolved to change. What could I do? Leave him because he was working hard? So I concentrated on being a restful, devoted wife.

"Gradually, after a few more weeks, the feeling about his job began to lessen. We resumed intercourse. I assured him that I did not disapprove of his attitudes toward his work, or toward me."

A year later, the couple had their first child, and the wife is again pregnant as I write this.

Preoccupation with other drives, of course, can be a cause of marital tensions on many levels. At times, the drives play themselves out in a short time. At times, a husband and wife can compromise the demands of a particular drive simply by rescheduling their lives a bit, by taking a long week end out of town or by making time for relaxation. If the drive is obsessive, lasting for many weeks or months and thus depriving the couple of healthy sexuality, it's time to see a counselor. Fortunately, most drives are likely not to be so obsessive in nature.

Small Nuisances—and Big Tensions

There are a great many obstacles to successful sexuality in marriage that can be labeled "mechanical." They range far and wide—from the creaky bed which disturbs the husband or wife, or fear of being overheard, to discomfort because of the time, place or the conditions under which one or the other partner desires sex.

Many women are reluctant to have intercourse in the morning or afternoon. It does not fit in with their romantic concepts and ideals. Husbands must understand this. Many wives refuse to have intercourse while visiting in someone else's home, on deserted beaches, or on couches, or in a parked car. All of these and many more upset some women's sensitivities. Disagreement over such matters can cause tension.

Here again, husbands and wives must make a real effort to understand each other's drives and motives. Open discussion of differences of feeling can help greatly. Also, retaining one's sense of dignity, humor and respect for the other's wishes can help immensely.

I mention humor because it is important in allaying sexual tensions. Sometimes, sex in marriage degenerates into a grim, forbidding, unwholesome ritual, completely devoid of any feeling of fun. Part of the reason is that the couple forgets to see the funny side of things.

I cannot help recalling one case in which a wife complained to her doctor that she could not bear to have intercourse with her husband. After a little probing the reason came out: her husband ate raw onions almost every night before retiring!

Understandably, the doctor had to restrain himself from smiling. Here was an essentially funny situation, but neither husband nor wife could see it that way. As a result, they did not attempt to cope with the essential problem—the onions. They began to sulk and the husband became enraged when his wife refused his advances.

The situation cleared up when the husband visited the doctor and simply agreed not to eat onions before going to bed. It was a good deal later that they began to see how funny the whole thing had been. Much better if they could have laughed about it earlier in the game—preferably in bed.

Husbands and wives should remember that a bath before bed will remove unpleasant body odors that may result after a long, hot day at the office or in the kitchen. Devotees of morning showers can still take them, but they should not skip the evening bath.

Body odors can be and usually are sexually stimulating, but not when they are excessive or stale. Women are particularly sensitive to accumulated body odors. The male body retains a pleasing masculine odor even after bathing—and will then be far more appealing to the wife.

I have listed ten extremely common factors which tend to make for tensions in sexual matters.

Logically you might ask whether there is any way before marriage to insure against such tensions. The answer is a resounding *yes*. You can do many things for yourself to help bridge the gap between the moral and social dictates of "no-sex" or limited sex in courtship, and full social and religious sanction for sex in marriage.

You'll recall that a fundamental aim of this book is to help you to edit the parts of your memory film and experience which may have given rise to unhealthy attitudes concerning sex, and to replace them with facts, with perspective and with confidence concerning sex in marriage. In the next chapter, I want to talk about ways toward release of sexual tensions, and in the one after that about preparation for marriage and the price paid in marriage when there is inadequate preparation.

4

Toward Release from Sexual Tensions

There is something about a new beginning that appeals to everyone. In the newness itself, there is a single crystalline moment, beautiful and uncluttered. The new marriage is like this in many ways. The day of the wedding ceremony shines crystal-clear and there is a breathless moment when all of the old becomes transmuted into the new.

Everything will be perfect, newlyweds believe, because everything is new. But is it? As we pointed out earlier, newlyweds bring a lifetime of attitudes, learning and experience into marriage. Has everything really changed? The newly married discover that it has not—a day, a week, a month or so after the wedding day.

They may learn, too, that the one big factor they had counted on to keep everything right, wonderful and perfect—namely, the physical love of marriage—is not perfect. It is not the transcendental light that floods every minute of the marriage with glory. Far from it!

Inevitably, tensions arise. And with them come self-doubt, disappointment and perhaps recrimination. How to cope with the tensions? Here are eight steps helpful in achieving release from sexual tensions in marriage. From these stem still others. Let's consider the eight, one at a time.

You Are Not Alone

Anxieties at one time or another concerning the physical aspects of marriage are virtually universal. You and just about everyone else you know has had them. Realizing this fully and accepting it is, in itself, good for you. It is therapeutic. Tension leads to further tension when you feel alone in your troubles. You are not alone. For one thing another human being shares your problem most intimately, your mate. It is certainly not realistic to consider yourself a special case, somehow victimized by a fate reserved only for you.

Take Your Time

I am amazed that married couples believe that the tinsel and gaiety of courtship, the wedding plans and the wedding day itself set a tone of inevitable, immediate success in sexuality. Of course, this is utter nonsense. There are almost always fits and starts, failures and successes, happinesses and heartaches. Most authorities believe that sexual adjustment in marriage rarely comes within a few months, and most successful husbands and wives admit this.

A good many believe that it rarely comes before one, three, five years, or even longer. Physical love, after all, is not something that can be regulated automatically as you would some mechanical device. It is an expression of the union of two people as one, a beautiful but intricate union that demands learning and effort. Remember, two people are involved, with their differing beliefs, sensitivities and desires. It takes time, effort, concentration, exploration and deep understanding to make a physical union increasingly rewarding. But time is what most marriages have plenty of—a lifetime. Don't rush it.

Be Ready to Unfix Your Fixed Beliefs

Of course, husband and wife enter marriage with a great many fixed ideas, but such ideas can hinder sexual compatibility. So, open your mind. Wipe the film record of your mind clean, or at least edit it so that you will not be hindered by fixed ideas or prejudices. This must be done to establish rapport with your spouse in a mature fashion. With an open mind, flexibility replaces rigidity, and flexibility is what you really need to achieve sexual fulfillment.

I recall a patient who revealed to his doctor that his wife insisted that it was wrong to have intercourse more than once a week. She maintained that she was perfectly content with the once-a-week schedule. Naturally, this rigid concept made for a good many anxieties in the marriage. The truth is, of course, that there is no "right" and "wrong" when it comes to frequency of intercourse. There is no arbitrary standard—just as there is no arbitrary standard of right and wrong in any other phase of sexuality in marriage. Well-adjusted married couples have learned how to agree together, within the confines of their own privacy, on their standards as to frequency of intercourse, sex play and all other matters concerning sex. And they change the standards as they themselves change.

Many people (especially women) inquire as to "proper" forms of stimulation, "proper" ways to reach the climax. I always tell them the same thing: *anything* is proper so long as it pleases both husband and wife and allows both to achieve emotional peace.

Not long ago, a young woman said to me: "Before we were married, my husband was in the Service, stationed in France. While there, he learned all sorts of things from girls about oral stimulation. Is this really proper?"

My answer remains the same. If the husband has strong feelings concerning one or another method of stimulation, he should discuss them candidly with his wife. She should do the same. Open exchange of desires should provide the basis for agreement. Such exchange is certain to decrease anxiety and to free both to experiment, to try, to discover. There is no fixed "right and wrong" in this regard. A man and his wife answer only to themselves and to each other in this area of their living.

Learn How to Compromise

After all, men and women are different, emotionally and organically. Thus, there must be compromise. Men are more easily stimulated, have more sexual fantasies and usually are more aggressive. Women tend to accept the romantic ideal to a far greater extent. They tend to dream romantically rather than act. They are not as easily stimulated and, as a rule, are less likely to play the role of the aggressor.

Considering these differences and countless others, compromise is an absolute necessity. The happily married couple is the one that has, through the years, made acceptable compromises concerning frequency of intercourse, method, time and place. Lack of compromise only serves to heighten sexual incompatibility. But compromise must never be one-sided.

Discard the Idea That Physical Love Is Everything in Marriage

Sex rarely can save a shaky marriage, but a full, understanding and beautiful marriage can save a shaky sexual relationship. Without a marriage compatible aside from sex, there can hardly be a full sex life.

Fundamentally, sex in marriage goes far beyond its pure pleasure aspect, for it serves as the final bond, a true, ultimate expression of love. But if the love does not exist in the first place, how can there be perfect sex? A full sex life in marriage is not likely to sustain a marriage that has little else of quality. If you believe that sex can be everything, you are in for a major disappointment. Love must come first, then sex—not the reverse. If you remember this you will spare yourself needless anguish in marriage.

Don't Rely on Tricks and Techniques

A great deal has been written on the subject of techniques of love-making in marriage. I do not believe that the techniques are valueless. On the contrary, married couples should have a sound knowledge of them and should be willing to experiment and to learn new ones.

But the belief that love tricks will sustain your sex life is naïve. Tricks of any kind are but momentary diversions. They are hardly the stuff that happy marital sexuality is made of. We are, after all, considering a profound human undertaking. The individual mainly preoccupied with sex techniques, the touches, caresses and other methods of arousal, is bound to run out of them. Then what?

The mature couple realizes that, as the years progress, there is constant new discovery about oneself and one's mate. Sex is never the same. Something exciting is always just ahead, if you will simply allow yourself a chance to discover it. This is natural and healthy. Those who relax in the idea that sex in marriage is a never-ending adventure with its own dynamism, its own unfolding wonder, rarely are disappointed.

Don't Be Ashamed to Seek Professional Advice

Many couples feel at ease talking to their next-door neighbors about their sexual problems, but are reluctant to talk to their doctors, ministers or a marriage counselor about them. This is sheer folly. There is a feeling on the part of many couples (it is probably most pronounced in men) that an admission of sexual apprehension and failure is a reflection of weakness and inadequacy.

What a fallacy! Married couples who have problems are so numerous that the problems themselves must be considered normal. Should a patient be ashamed of telling his doctor that he has influenza or faulty vision? The answer is obvious. And so is the answer as it applies to sexual matters.

We assume we need to learn a job. We know we must learn about virtually everything in family matters from cooking to raising children. We accept the learning process in almost every human endeavor. Yet many of us fail to see the wisdom of learning anything that has to do with sex.

This failure almost certainly intensifies sexual incompatibility, which of course leads to heightened sexual tensions. Our unwillingness to learn imposes anxiety after anxiety and perpetuates and heightens sexual frustrations, so that they can hardly emerge into the bright light of reason, clarity and ultimate solution.

A man I know refused for years to tell his doctor of his great anxiety about his sex activities. He went along unhappy, sour, convinced that he could never achieve sexual fulfillment.

Finally, one day, he blurted out the story of his misery to his doctor.

"I'm depressed, terribly depressed," he said. "For a long time, my wife and I have not enjoyed satisfying sexual relations. She accepts the situation as it is, but I cannot."

The patient, an obese fellow in his early forties, pointed out that his excess weight simply prevented him from being comfortable in intercourse. What is more, he was convinced that his obesity had lessened his sexual capacities.

His doctor discussed the matter with him, put him on a diet. The patient fully realized the motivation, the stake he had in losing weight. At the end of a few months, he had lost 29 pounds.

"I cannot tell you how this has helped us in every way," that patient said to his doctor. "Our sex life has never been as wonderful."

If that man had been able to seek help sooner, there would not have been those wasted years. In his story, there is a moral for all married couples who multiply their anxieties by failing to seek competent advice or to follow it after it is offered.

Two other cases can be cited briefly in this connection. The first involves a woman of twenty-seven, married five years, who would become periodically depressed and refuse to have intercourse with her husband. This went on for two years. When she finally visited her family doctor and discussed it with him, they found the cause of the depression—worries about her father and mother.

Once the cause was revealed, the depression lessened in intensity and she resumed normal sexual relations with her husband.

The second case involves a couple in their thirties who had the wisdom and initiative to consult a capable marriage counselor in their Midwestern home town. Their problem stemmed from the fact that the wife wanted to have intercourse only on week ends. She claimed that was the only time she could really relax.

After a few visits, the counselor convinced the wife that her husband was really not making outlandish demands on her and explained manual stimulation. In addition, the wife was persuaded that she should submit to intercourse occasionally during the week, even if she did not derive maximum satisfaction. In this case, the advice worked and the couple has enjoyed much improved sex for some time.

The point in all of these cases is that the individuals concerned were intelligent enough to seek and accept competent advice.

There Must Be Mutual Love and Respect

Perhaps this final consideration should have been first. It should be implicit in happy sexual relations that love and respect pervade the marriage. Why mention it? Isn't this self-evident? Perhaps.

But there is much evidence that anxiety-ridden couples do fail to respect each other. Many do fail to approach sex with the necessary humility, tenderness and gentleness that should typify any part of marriage, but especially this part. This failure is the source of a great deal of tension in regard to marital sex.

What does respect for the other person mean? Simply that the other person's needs and feelings are truly more important to you than your own. This is something that cannot be faked. It is either so or not so. When it becomes so for both partners, the marriage—and sex—are on the way to success.

5

An Ounce of Prevention . . .

The importance of preventive medicine is well recognized today in combating illness. All possible efforts are made to decrease the possibility of coming down with one or another disease. We take shots against polio, tetanus, smallpox, diphtheria and typhoid, to mention but a few. However, insofar as marriage is concerned, we very often fail to see the value of prevention.

Pre-marriage counseling courses, as offered by the Roman Catholic Church, marriage counseling services, Planned Parenthood, the YM and YWCA's and by some religious leaders and institutions, are just the type of preventive medicine needed by countless couples to avert the sexual ailments and handicaps of marriage. Ideally, the prospective husband and wife should take the course together.

Some time ago, the daughter of a friend announced her engagement. I called to suggest that she might be interested in attending a series of lectures for engaged couples.

"Oh, but I'm much too busy," she said. "I have my job; I have to get my trousseau and pick a wedding dress. Then there are all the showers."

And I thought to myself, "Yes, but you won't even spend a few evenings in the company of your fiancé getting to know something about this tremendous adventure upon which you are about to embark."

I said to her, "Frances, this has to do with your *life,* the most important part of your life."

"I'm really too busy," she replied. And I felt extremely sorry for her.

Learning Before Marriage

Supposing she had attended this course, or any one of the many other fine education-for-marriage courses offered in the United States? What would she and her fiancé have found there?

Most such courses consist of lectures and discussion on motives for marriage, the spiritual side of marriage, emotional factors in marriage, the physical facts and the sex factor in marriage. These are conducted by physicians, ministers and trained marriage counselors. Discussions on sex would be likely to include discussion on sex in the honeymoon and thereafter, emotional overtones of sex and physical love as the years pass in marriage. Some courses also discuss financial planning and practical homemaking.

It's easy to see how valuable such a course can be, not only because you learn facts you may not have known before, but because such courses represent one of the few opportunities you and your fiancé will have to meet before marriage for straightforward consideration of marriage itself. Experts present the course material and you and your fiancé participate along with other young couples about to be married.

Openly and freely you can discuss many things, including the real meaning of sex in marriage, anxieties that are bound to crop up and how to resolve those anxieties. With your fiancé you have a chance to measure each other's reactions concerning many delicate matters. This certainly helps you to become more fully acquainted with each other.

If a reaction or attitude in the course troubles you, you have a chance to sit down, question it, talk it out together before you are actually involved in marriage. This is where preventive medicine comes in. Here is the opportunity to explore, disagree and resolve your differences *before* they occur in the marriage.

Further, you have a chance in the friendly atmosphere of the group to articulate the word *sex*, explore it, examine it and come to realize that it and what it represents need not be frightening. Suddenly, too, you realize that you are not alone in your feelings about sex, whatever they may be. The other young couples in the course are experiencing them, too. This in itself provides a large dose of preventive medicine.

This feeling of not being alone is tremendously important. It is a great discovery that most of us make at one time or another. Nothing that you feel or that has happened to you is unique. Your feelings have been felt by not one but by thousands and millions of others. Your experiences likewise have occurred in the lives of countless others. This, in itself, is a great source of reassurance and it applies to all phases of marriage.

You Cannot Know "All About Sex"

You might protest secretly to yourself, "Why should I bother to spend my time taking a course? Not only have I read about sex, but I have had sex experience. I know all about it!"

I have two answers for you in relation to this argument. A young couple just beginning sexual life has a tendency to think that successful sex experience is a matter of tricks and techniques. This is not entirely their fault. Rather it is the fault of the very books they have been consulting, which tend to overemphasize the importance of techniques.

The great determining factor in the success of any human relationship is *how you feel about the other person,* not how you *think* you feel, but rather how you *really* feel. That is why groups of young couples coming together under experienced leadership to explore the future marriage relationship make such a valuable investment in time and spiritual energy.

"Of course," you say, "I know how I feel about my fiancé. It's love." This answer is not a final one, nor is it necessarily a good one. For it to be a good answer depends upon the *kind* of love you feel. There are as many ways of loving as there are people in the world.

My second answer to the young people who believe they already are well indoctrinated in sex experience is this: nobody ever knows all about sex. The most remarkable fact about sex is that it is never the same and is always new. It changes as you change and as your partner changes. And both of you are changing every minute that you live. Even if you've already experienced sex, a preparation-for-marriage course can be of great value in helping you relate the past and the future in a realistic way.

Experience Enhances Sex

A marriage preparation course will help you become aware of still another fundamental concerning sex. Because many couples fear what the years will do to their sex drive, they should know that the sexual experiences of a husband and his wife in their forties, fifties and even later can be beyond any power to describe, deeper and more enthralling than in their twenties.

The reasons are numerous. In middle age, the couple already has lived and loved together for many years. They have explored on a wide frontier the beauties and satisfactions of sex. They have weathered many storms together. Gone is the superficiality and sham. Now, after the poses, the stresses and strains of the earlier years, there is no longer need for pretense. They feel free and at ease with each other in their sexual expression.

Furthermore, middle-aged couples have emerged from the child-bearing years. Thus, they need no longer cope with the inevitable anxieties of possible pregnancy. A woman past menopause very often feels emancipated, and many have told me, "Now I can really enjoy sex." Significantly, the sexual drives of many women accelerate after menopause for just this reason.

Indeed, there is even sexual satisfaction in store for the elderly. We rarely see or hear anything about sexual fulfillment in persons aged sixty and beyond. Yet we know that many are physically capable and we know, too, that sex is important to many couples in the past-sixty, so-called geriatric age range. Despite what you have been conditioned to believe, sex in this stage of life can be as vital a force for couples as it is two, three or four decades earlier.

Not long ago, a man in his late sixties and I were discussing this very question. In his gentle and tender manner, he wanted to know why people disregarded or scoffed at the importance of sex among the aging.

"Is a kiss more vital or more important to a person in his twenties than in his sixties?" he asked. "Is a caress more meaningful depending on whether your hair has yet turned gray? Isn't a touch still an expression of love, no matter how old you are?"

Such questions obviously are rhetorical, for age does not lessen the importance of sex. A gifted artist had an active and satisfying sex life almost to the time he contracted a fatal disease at the age of eighty-six. There are many other similar cases in this age range.

We have seen that there are certain fundamentals needed to prepare oneself for marriage and to build in marriage a strong foundation for sexual fulfillment. We have seen, too, that there are a wide variety of factors which can prevent the full realization of physical love in marriage. There are still other problems.

The Dangers of an Incomplete Sex Life

We can state with certainty that lack of sexual fulfillment contributes to the rate of divorce and to the incidence of extramarital entanglement. It has been estimated that anywhere from 10 to 25 percent of all married men indulge in extramarital sex activity at some time in their married lives. Undoubtedly, this is true. Among women, the rate is probably lower.

Thus, there are two gross and obvious dangers in sexual incompleteness. In the first, divorce, there is physical dissolution of the home. In the second, involving extramarital "straying," there is spiritual dissolution of the home. Both are tragic and obvious for all the world to see.

However, the more subtle manifestations of the incomplete sex life are not as obvious. Sometimes you meet a couple who are slightly argumentative, short with each other, somewhat aloof from each other. This may signal sexual disappointment over a long period of time. You ask, "Why do they stay married?" Often, the answer lies in the fact that they have become passive about each other. They regard each other as necessary, but not overwhelmingly important. Their passivity prevents them from taking positive steps in any direction.

Thus, they do not face their sexual problem squarely, but sink into defeat. In a similar fashion, they do not face the vital problems of their marriage squarely. They drag on and on. Society frowns on divorce and that fact deters some from divorce. Also it may be convenient to remain married, or they may remain together for "the sake of the children" or for the benefit of the outside world. They remain in a kind of torpor, which renders them boring and unwholesome to themselves, to each other and, frequently, to others.

This is a central danger of incomplete sexuality in marriage. However, it can manifest itself in a thousand and one subtle ways. It represents an unhealthy and tragic situation, for it robs the couple of two great gifts, the gift of growth in life and the gift of enjoyment of life. And, too, it erodes love, so that their love may turn into hate, into deep anxiety or into a kind of neutralism in which the individual exists as a robot, but does not really live.

These are some of the common denominators of sex failure in marriage. If we learn about them ahead of time enough to understand them, we can act intelligently to forestall them. But a premarital training course may not go far enough.

To perform the task fully, as it should be done, we should return to the time in our lives when we first started learning about sex.

6

Early Sex Education and Experience

To understand your attitudes and emotions in marriage today, healthy or unhealthy, you must return to your years of growing up. For it is in those years that beliefs and ideas form and then are tempered by experience.

It is the purpose of this chapter to help you return to your early childhood and to demonstrate how what happened to you then, or did not happen, helps to make you the kind of person you are.

Let's dispel one widespread misconception before we go any further. You may be grown up and married now, but that does not mean you are fixed and unchangeable. Most people believe that adults cannot change significantly, but they are wrong.

I know a man of eighty who is still changing, still learning, still achieving. He is an artist who feels strongly that he has not yet finished growing. He works, travels, studies and has a well-rounded social life. I know that he never will stop growing as a person—not until the final great learning experience.

In marriage, in our careers, in everything we set out to achieve, we must realize that we as human beings have a marvelous potential that permits us forever to continue to learn, to improve, to expand our horizons. We need never be fixed and unchanging if we don't want to be.

A good many people fail to recognize the qualities in us which make for limitless opportunity. Because of childhood experience they establish a pattern, sometimes an unhealthy pattern, and persist in living by that pattern. They refuse change.

It's a pity. For we can recall our childhood experiences and teaching, examine the things that happened to us, or didn't, and then, because of this miraculous capacity of human beings to change if they want to, we can correct the things that went wrong. This is much more than a second chance. It is an ever-present chance. We should use it.

The Beginning of Sex Education

Earlier, I mentioned that sex education begins just after birth. Very early, the baby can sense the difference between the father and the mother, and responds to those differences in varied ways but with equal love. For the qualities of maleness appeal to a baby in certain ways and the qualities of femaleness appeal to him in different ways.

Quite unconsciously, as the child grows up, he absorbs knowledge and feelings about the relationship between that man and that woman who live together, his parents. At first, he applies the knowledge and feelings to all men and women. Later, as he approaches maturity, he applies those feelings to himself.

In the ideal home atmosphere, the parents can and do talk to their children about all human relationships. Thus, the children have an opportunity to question freely all that they see and hear. The knowledge and understanding they acquire in this way bolster their consciences, their sense of honesty, their sense of social and moral values.

If the child is thus fortunate enough to grow up in this kind of home, in which the predominating theme is honesty, candor and reasoned discipline along with a warm and loving parental relationship, he is likely to have a sound outlook on sex, for the wonderful qualities of such a home radiate this kind of understanding.

However, this is the ideal, and does not always exist. Something short of the mark does, though, in a great many homes. Let's say that the father of a growing child is interested primarily in getting ahead. He has enough education so that he can achieve success in the line of work he has selected, but he never was much of a reader or a thinker. He confuses action with accomplishment, speed with industriousness. He is apt to judge other people's feelings by his own and his own are determined quite often by what he feels is safe.

He is honest, but he lacks imagination. His leisure activities reflect this. He likes baseball in the summer and television shows in the winter. He's kind, but, you'll recall, more than a little preoccupied with business success. Thus, most of his conversations with other members of his family deal with work and its obligations, food, TV and movies, the car, relatives and the annual vacation. The latter is spent fishing, so that he can "unwind."

The mother, his wife, also is a fairly uncomplicated person. When someone asks her what she does, her reply is, "I take care of the house." She likes to read the women's magazines and watch television shows. She has a fairly well-set daily routine, which involves housework, getting the children off to school and cooking. (She is likely not to want to break her kitchen habits by delving into new recipes, for she feels she has been through that stage.)

Occasionally, she attends a parent-teacher meeting, but her feeling is that civic participation should be left to those who have more time. As you can see, both the father and mother in this family are fundamentally almost totally concerned with the mechanics of living.

The wife loves her husband, who, she feels, is loyal, hard-working, a good provider and kind to her. Their sex life is rather a secret one. For two or three years after she was married, or perhaps for even a longer period, she was glad her husband took such pleasure in sex, but she wondered what all the fuss was about. She felt then that sex was a rather mechanical thing, an obligation of marriage, nothing more.

Then, all at once, she began to discover sexual pleasure herself. She began to respond to her husband. When that happened, both of them accepted the change without mentioning it to each other. Although they have continued to enjoy it mutually, she has never gotten over a slight feeling of guilt. She wonders vaguely if her husband possibly thinks of her as "bad" for sometimes meeting him more than halfway sexually.

Now you have a fairly clear picture of this family, which really is quite a good one because the essential relationship is one of harmony. There are no very great upheavals, no great ups and downs, no overwhelming conflicts, no boundless joys or monumental achievements. The father and mother do not quarrel seriously. Essentially, they are contented together.

What is missing here? A great intellectual drive? Not at all, for why should everyone be intellectual? Here is a family carrying on some of the world's work and contributing a harmonious home; yet even so, something is missing. This lack may be felt deeply later on when the children of the home grow into adulthood.

Lack of Communication

What is missing in this home is verbal communication in contrast to the nonverbal kind I spoke of earlier. This lack may have its effect in emotional problems concerning sex in the later lives of the children. These parents do not discuss with each other anything that is really important about their feelings. Neither do they communicate their feelings on important matters to their children.

What I have described here is a quite typical family situation. When the children were young, their mother passed on to them a small amount of sex information in a rather embarrassed fashion—at least, they learned from her where babies come from. Since then, the children have "learned" much more about sex from their friends in school. But have they? Their parents would be amazed at what the children think about sex.

Some of it is accurate. But the parents are likely to be so limited in their total understanding that they would be unable to separate accuracy from inaccuracy. In any event, the son in this family is growing into puberty with all of its changes, and the daughter is coming into adolescence. But never once have the parents, either alone or together, talked to the youngsters about the dynamic bodily changes taking place. Nor have they spoken to the children about the kinds of feelings they can expect to have, what they might do to try to handle those feelings, or the standards of sexual conduct that the world expects of them. Nor do the parents approach any of the hundreds of questions that youngsters find extremely confusing as they grow up.

If parents have never discussed such matters with each other, they are not likely to attempt it with their children. And if they never broach the subject to the children, how can they expect the children to develop any clear-cut mode of behavior regarding sex, either before or after marriage?

Where Did You Get Sex Information?

I would like to ask the reader a question. Where and how did you develop your ideas and attitudes with regard to prostitution? Can you remember back to the time when you first became aware that the sex relationship can and does occur outside of marriage? Then, do you remember when you first discovered that the sex relationship need not have anything to do with loving a person, but can become a part of a commercial transaction?

This is a very hard and ugly fact for young people to accept and become accustomed to. If it is first presented to a young person simply as one of many ugly facts about sex, a grave injustice has been done him. For the young person, that explanation may represent the entire sexual relationship, making it ugly and forbidding.

Instead, the explanation should place prostitution in perspective, so that the young person is made aware of the fact that prostitution and promiscuity are perversions of the real meaning of sex. If he fails to get this idea, his sensitivity and understanding of sex may be blunted. He may adopt the attitude that sex is essentially dirty, representing only the seamy side of life, and that is what it may then become in his own life.

Remember, I asked if you could recall when and how the concept of prostitution first came to you. I have a reason for asking this. It is extremely useful in clearing up our ideas on any subject to return to our own initial experiences with it and to review our memory film sequences. Thus, we can determine how we first began to learn and absorb ideas about which we often become confused later in life. Sex, of course, is one of the areas in which we become most confused, because sex is surrounded by such excitement, curiosity, guilt and other disturbing emotions.

How Early Experiences Can Affect You

The following examples will clarify this important point. A young man I know told his doctor that sex really revolted him. He became excited by sex play, but disliked himself for the excitement. Intercourse with his wife was considered by him to be extremely distasteful. He developed elaborate excuses to avoid it.

He pleaded fatigue, illness, pain, and devised many other excuses to avoid physical love. Of course, this caused a crisis in his marriage. He was guilt-ridden, unhappy and verging on desperation. To him, the problem appeared insoluble.

The doctor asked him to recall his early boyhood experiences. This was difficult, as it is for many people. The process was time-consuming, but this young husband was mature enough to recognize that he needed help, so he returned for visit after visit to the doctor.

Finally, the young man remembered vaguely an incident which he had never before recalled in his adulthood. As a boy of seven or eight, he had been in the playground when he spotted another young boy doing something odd. He walked up to him and found that the other youngster, about the same age, was fondling his penis. At first our young man remembered watching the boy out of curiosity. Later, he became intrigued by what the other boy was doing.

His mother came along at just that moment. She saw what was going on and whisked her son away. First, he recalled, she spanked him. Then she delivered a blistering lecture to him. She told him his father would deal with him later when he came home from work. She told him that if she ever found him around that other little boy again, there would be harsh discipline. She warned him that if he ever masturbated, there would be even harsher discipline.

From then on, the young man recalled, his parents began to mention the incident to him and to each other. Each time they alluded to it they took on a grim and forbidding air. The young husband recalled that several times in the next year when he was spanked, his mother or father would remark, "You haven't been the same since that day at the playground."

In other words, that single incident colored significantly the whole subsequent life and growth of that child. His parents normally were strict and harsh in their discipline, and their constant close association of discipline with sexuality left its mark on the young man.

With the doctor's guidance, the husband became able to understand and accept that his own attitudes toward sex were influenced in a most important fashion by his feelings of guilt and the prospect of punishment. Thus, sex to this husband meant that he would be punished somehow for what he had come to believe was a dirty, wrongful act.

Realization of this all-important factor came slowly, of course. It seemed incredible to the husband that his attitudes could have been so firmly established by his early experiences, experiences which he could barely recall.

Gradually, as the husband understood the source of his problem, his own attitudes and beliefs began to change. He began to understand the real meaning of sex in marriage. He became able genuinely to desire intercourse. He began to read, to learn the facts about his body and his wife's. I am happy to say that today, that couple has two children. They report their sex life as beautiful and highly rewarding. Thus, the husband, by recalling his early experiences, by delving into his memory, was helped to discover the key to a new and fuller life in marriage.

The second case I shall relate deals with a young woman who believed that she was frigid and could never achieve sexual fulfillment in her marriage. She told a marriage counselor in a Midwestern city the following story:

She had been married four and a half years. Prior to the marriage, her fiancé, now her husband, wanted to have intercourse with her, but she refused. He apparently felt two ways about the refusal. He was annoyed, but he also felt admiration for her. Prior to marriage they had petted considerably, but she did not especially enjoy the touches and embraces.

On their honeymoon, she complained to her husband that intercourse was painful for her and that they had best show restraint. Through the four and a half years of marriage, she, like the young husband in the previous case, made innumerable excuses to avoid intercourse.

Her husband was extremely unhappy about this state of affairs and talked to her about the possibility of separation; it was this threat that brought her to a marriage counselor. In subsequent visits, the husband accompanied her to the counselor's office. After a few sessions, the counselor casually asked her to dig back into her life and try to pinpoint a factor or a group of factors which had caused her to feel that she was frigid.

At first she could recall nothing of significance. Then she remembered something that she said could not really be relevant, but that she related to the marriage counselor and to her husband.

On the corner, close to the house in which she grew up, there had lived a bachelor in his late forties. He was a huge, ungainly man, not at all physically attractive. He was even more forbidding to young children because he had a scraggly black beard.

All the adults up and down the block considered him a strange and mysterious person not worth befriending. Thus, to all the children on the block, parents had given the order to stay away from that man, his house and his back yard.

One afternoon, our young wife recalled, she happened to be passing the bearded man's house. At the time she was about eleven years old.

The shades were up, the curtains were thin and transparent, and she was able to see the bearded man stark naked with a nude young woman. They were running about the house, pausing now and again for a feverish embrace or a sensual touch. The eleven-year-old girl stood on the sidewalk, fascinated.

After a few minutes, the woman sat down on a couch with the man next to her. It was then that the watching child began to realize that because of their proximity and behavior the nude figures must be having intercourse.

She went home and told her mother, in all innocence, what she had just observed. Her mother showed no anger. Rather, she began a long discussion on the "evils" of sex and told her daughter to blot out of her mind what she had just seen; and, of course, she forbade her daughter to go anywhere near that man's house again.

The mother and, later, the father of that eleven-year-old took it upon themselves to erase what they felt was a terrible and forbidding experience for their daughter. They feared that she would be forever affected by having inadvertently viewed the "awful scene."

So they set about to tell her about "nice girls" and how they behaved. They so exaggerated the restrictions of normal sexual behavior that their daughter grew up with the idea firmly rooted that proper sexual behavior for a young wife was to indulge in practically no sex at all.

Her parents associated a great many things with sex, she recalled. As a teen-ager, she remembered, her parents told her often that many crimes of violence were sex-determined. She began to believe that many persons, men and women, were "oversexed" and that this was a common malady of the times. The net effect of her beliefs was that sex was a curse, that it caused most people to behave in abnormal ways. She believed, too, that nothing good could come of sex in marriage.

Of course, the mere fact that she faced the realities of her problem actually relieved the problem to some extent. But it took a good deal of patience and understanding on the part of the marriage counselor and her husband to give her a new orientation on the subject of marital sex.

Today, that couple's married life has improved greatly. All the problems are not yet solved, for every once in a while the wife recalls the strong emotional pulls of her formative years and must struggle with them anew. But she is now able to view the entire subject of sex in marriage with some degree of equilibrium, and one result is that her own marriage is no longer threatened. She and her husband see themselves as having made great progress. They are happy to spend more time in working out the remaining problems.

My point in relating these two cases is this: both the young husband and the wife found they could alleviate their problems, first by facing them, then by seeking competent help, and finally, by digging back into their experience to find the cause of their trouble, or at least a significant part of the cause. This is in part how psychiatry works. But not all people need psychiatry, and it is worth while doing as much as you can by yourself to find out where the trouble might have started.

It is important to note still another point in this connection. In both cases, parents and their attitudes contributed in an important way to the distortion of sex in the minds of the two people I have discussed. The parents themselves had distorted viewpoints and passed them on to their youngsters.

Thus, the children were deprived of accurate information. They were deprived of a view of sex that had some perspective, and they failed to gain a comfortable feeling about the subject. The children failed to grow up understanding the development of the sexual process in themselves, the place of sex in the world and some of the ways in which sexual processes occur among other people in our world.

Factors That Can Form Your Sex Beliefs

Little boys and girls somehow get the idea that when you are married, you immediately have a baby. At an early stage children view this as an automatic process. By the age of seven or eight, they begin to realize that it is not automatic, and to get the idea that you must "do something" in order to have the baby. It is obvious that the baby is being carried within the mother and that the father has had something important and mysterious to do with the entire process.

However, all too often the ideas that youngsters have on the subject are vague and full of misconceptions. Even seventh- and eighth-grade boys and girls may have extremely distorted ideas about the sex and birth acts. Then sooner or later, there comes a moment when a child gains awareness that it is possible for a baby to be born outside of marriage. This, of course, also means to the child that the sex act can be performed outside of marriage. This may be a real shock to the child concerning sex.

Another shock may come when the child suddenly realizes that it is perfectly possible to participate in a sex act that does not result in a baby. This is still another vital realization on the part of the child. He can now see that there is a purpose to the sex act besides sheer procreation. Once again, when the child first becomes aware of this, the parent is obligated to put into focus marital sex, to point out that it serves as a magnificent expression of married love as well as for the purpose of procreation.

Still another shock may come later. The child at this point associates the sex act only with the concept of love. Having discovered that marriage, sex and babies are not inevitably linked, he now discovers that marriage, sex and love also are not always so linked.

Sex and Love Can Exist Apart

Finally, he learns that it is possible even to separate the act of sex from the feeling of love and that such a separation is not a rare but a frequent occurrence. When this realization sweeps over the youngster, there is, I believe, a very destructive moment, and his parents must help him to cope with it.

These shocking concepts come to the child through a variety of sources. Street-corner friends, unthinking adults, books and sensational newspapers and magazines are but a few of the more common sources. What happens? The young person exposed to such information becomes confused. He doesn't know what to believe. On one side he is told one thing, on the second side he is told another. The seeds of conflict have been sown.

The immediate need is for someone to provide an explanation for what, to the youngster, appear to be contradictory ideas about sex. Now, if his parents are uncommunicative about the subject, or if they cloak it in mystery or in any way represent sex as being forbidding, they only contribute to the conflict.

If the youngster is left to flounder without knowledge, without perspective, sex becomes something destructive and negative, something about which he can never feel warm and good.

Avoiding Sex Shocks

If, however, there is an adult, preferably the father or mother, with whom the child has always been able to communicate warmly and trustingly, these seeming inconsistencies about sex and all else on the subject can be talked about calmly and without damaging emotion.

The parents can explain that there are many facts about life which must be faced in all their crudity. For instance, the parents can point out that man has never yet learned full respect for human life and thus we still have murder and wars; that man often fails to show full respect for other human beings and thus we still have exploitation of underprivileged groups.

These critical subjects and others must be discussed in the safety and security of the home. Keeping our young people in ignorance simply won't work. We rationalize it by saying to ourselves that we are keeping them in innocence. Too often, this leads to disastrous results in the young person himself.

How often I have heard from a young man or woman exclamations like: "Why, I simply did not know the facts . . ." "I was never allowed to discuss such matters . . ." "Our home was so strict we were not to speak unless spoken to . . ." "Proper people don't discuss it . . ." "That is street-corner talk . . ." "Do nice people really do those things?" All of these in relation to some sex problem which may have been unsolved for a good many years, and one that may have caused untold anxiety and unhappiness, and created great sexual tensions within the marriage.

We must develop in our children the strength to cope with a broad range of attitudes and emotions, no matter where these come from. Young people must understand the bad things of life as well as the success stories. They must learn how to carry on the good life in spite of pitfalls, in spite of antisocial behavior on the part of individuals, groups and societies.

To achieve this, young people need information, a helping hand now and again, firm guidance, affection and patience. All these can help build strength to face the task in any area of living. Parents, of course, are ideally situated to provide the vital ingredients for this strength.

Sex Discussion Early in Life

I suppose that most parents do not look forward to discussing sex with their sons and daughters. I have heard many say that it is a "thankless task." How ridiculous, for here is one of the most important privileges of living, and parents huff and puff when they think about it.

If a child inquires of his parents about a flagrant wrong involving sex, the parent would be wise not to sidestep the question, but to face it squarely, without pique and without discomfort. If this was not done when you were a child, it may account for some of your present-day tensions. A discussion concerning ways in which sex can go wrong should be followed by many talks between parent and child concerning the ways in which sex goes right and enriches the lives of so many persons. In other words, parents should strive to establish a "positive set" concerning sex in the minds of their children. They should be "letting their children in on a good thing" rather than warning them against a bad thing.

What must be emphasized? First the facts. And the facts are

that while sexual adjustment must be worked for, it is achieved by most couples; that sex is not an invitation to disaster, but rather a great and rewarding part of life.

For every sexual relationship that goes wrong, there are numberless others that proceed relatively smoothly and are well based in a secure and happy marriage. Parents who have laid the basis for understanding how good and sound sexual relationships develop, are safe to discuss with their children the ways in which sex can go wrong. In fact, they are obligated to do just this. Failure to fulfill the obligation can lead to later sexual tensions for their youngsters.

Understanding Homosexuality

It is vital for young people to know ahead of time what homosexuality is and how it can develop. Young people should be fully aware that at one time or another they will probably meet homosexuals. Their parents should prepare them for this by explaining the nature of homosexuality, the conflicts of the homosexual and his behavior patterns. Generally, it is agreed that homosexuality stems from deep and complex emotional problems developing from childhood. Therefore, it should be viewed as an illness requiring help and treatment, not as something dangerous requiring punishment. Such explanations will go far to alleviate fear, surprise and confusion between the young people themselves and the homosexual who already carries a burden of social disapproval.

It is almost inevitable in our culture, I think, that a boy will, sometime during his life, be the subject of a homosexual advance. How much better if his father has ahead of time helped the boy understand the situation, so that when he meets it he will feel competent to cope with it. If there is no prior understanding of homosexuality, the boy will quite understandably overreact, thereby harming himself as well as the sick person who approached him.

Now you can see why I suggested that you run your film memory record over again and try to pick out those moments when new ideas came to you about all aspects of sex. If your parents were like those I described previously, good people, fundamentally happy and contented, but still unable to talk to you in a way that might have prepared you to understand the varied aspects of sex, you have probably faced many dilemmas. There probably have been many places along the line where gaps in your knowledge and understanding of the whole sweep of sexual experience produced confusion or even harmful situations. Further, these gaps may have produced feelings of fear, of shame, of guilt and perhaps of revulsion, or even of sexual desire so strong that it frightened you.

You pay a price for these feelings if you do not understand them. For when the time comes to establish your own sex life with your lifetime partner, these feelings can interfere greatly with the proper establishment of your sexual relationship.

Furthermore, there is still another vital area of consideration in this connection. If these feelings run unchecked, you, as a parent, are liable to repeat the mistakes of your own parents. When the time comes for you to start providing sex education for your youngsters, these same feelings will interfere with what should be the smooth flow of communication between you and your children. This is why it is doubly important for you, as early as possible, to return to your own early experiences and straighten out the ideas and feelings you have about sex and to fill in the gaps in your knowledge.

How to Unwind Your Memory Film

Supplanting old ideas and emotions with new ones may not be an easy thing to achieve. If you are seriously ill emotionally, that is to say, if the feelings of guilt, shame and fear are so powerful that they interfere actively with all your relationships, you need psychiatric help. Fortunately, only some of us need this either on a short-term or long-term basis.

The rest of us, if we are strong and intelligent, will say to ourselves, "I will not allow the inevitable mistakes of my parents to cripple me, particularly in the critical area of the closest human relationships I will ever have, with my mate and with my children.

"I will set about to try to change the old ideas which have brought me so much unhappiness. I will read intelligently to obtain accurate information about all phases of sexual life. As I read, I will examine the feelings I have regarding what I read.

"I will question my prior convictions on any aspect of sex in the light of new information. I will make an earnest effort to remember the feelings I had when I first learned about sex as a child, then because I am no longer a child but a mature adult, I will re-examine those feelings to determine if they were truly valid and necessary. I will re-examine them, too, to assess their importance in my present-day sexual attitudes and behavior.

"Then, if I cannot resolve my problem myself, or with the help of my spouse, I will seek some wise person with whom I can consult about my feelings. It might be my minister because many ministers these days have had special training in counseling about sex and marriage. It could be my doctor, especially if he had some psychiatric training in medical school, or has interested himself in psychiatric teaching since he began his practice. Of course, turning to my minister or my doctor will prove especially rewarding if he himself is a wise and patient person who enjoys a happy married life.

"I might turn to a mature friend whose experience has helped him or her in gaining knowledge of human problems. For instance, the friend might be a nurse, a social worker, a psychologist. And, believe it or not, it could even be one or both of my parents. This is because I now realize that since I have grown up, it has become much easier for me to talk to my parents on all sorts of intimate subjects, and, as we talk, to put into words thoughts that never before were allowed to come up."

If, concerning sex in marriage, people adopted a credo embodying this kind of honesty with themselves, there would be far fewer sexual crises in marriage. For release from sexual tensions can be achieved only if the individual is willing to probe or to allow others to help him probe the sources of the tensions themselves.

Earlier, I used prostitution as an example of a subject that, through a lifetime, can conjure up all sorts of misconceptions and negative feelings about sex. There are other subjects that can achieve the same negative result.

Your Attitudes Toward Masturbation

Most of our parents were brought up by their parents to believe that masturbation is a very bad practice. Years ago it was said to be the cause of disease, of feeble-mindedness and of various other disasters. Indeed these beliefs still persist and are still handed down from parent to child. Aside from masturbation's supposed implications for health, there are also said to be moral implications. Some people still believe that masturbation is a deep sin and a significant sign of immorality. In addition, most people, I think, still cling to the idea that masturbation should be stopped, by force if necessary.

Actually, medical science tells us that masturbation is not a "habit," but is one of the quite normal experiences of growing up. Most small children do it perhaps without even thinking of it or, for that matter, knowing what they are doing. That is, until their parents' admonitions make them feel shame and guilt.

Most adolescents of both sexes, whether they remember ever

having masturbated or not, do so at some time during their adolescence. Once again, this in itself absolutely is not harmful. However, the sense of guilt and fear which surrounds masturbation in the minds of parents can be exceedingly harmful to the youngsters. How? Because the parents convey to the minds of the children that they have performed an evil act. Sex, then, becomes associated with evil, and in the child's mind may never be associated with positive values, but may forever carry an aura of wrongdoing.

Masturbation Is Not Harmful

If a young person spends a good deal of time daydreaming and masturbating, this may indicate that he is in emotional trouble. You'll remember that I said "a good deal of time." If this happens, the child may be retreating from the real world. He may be expressing some deep-rooted feeling of inadequacy, jealousy or hostility. Such a child needs outside help as a rule.

In such cases, of course, the masturbation is a symptom of the problem, not a cause of it. Several questions must be answered in order to pinpoint the real cause. What compels this young person to expend his energies in masturbation? What is it that blocks him from assuming the normal play activities of his age group? What sense of frustration or failure is causing him to withdraw into himself, to seek his own body for comfort and release of tensions?

Once again, your own film memory record will have to be unwound and rerun. You will have to dig deep to discover what your attitude is, what it *really* is, toward masturbation. You will have to re-examine your attitudes in the bright, clear light of your present understanding. You are obligated to shake yourself loose from attitudes and emotions based on inadequate information or on improper teaching and experience.

Ideally, this type of re-examination on your own part should take place prior to marriage. By so doing, you will enter marriage without a holdover set of misguided beliefs. However, if you are already married, there is no time like the present for taking appropriate action.

Early Sexual Trauma

There are other ways in which a young person evolves distorted sexual notions. For instance, if some badly adjusted adult makes a sexual gesture to a child when he is very young, the child may feel the effects of this trauma for some time.

It is most important to remember the following in this connection: the act itself rarely is damaging to the child; rather it is the attitudes, actions and beliefs of the adults surrounding the child that are destructive.

Let's say that a little girl on her way to kindergarten suddenly sees a man exposing himself. Or the same little girl is touched about the genital organs by such a man, or is asked by the man to touch his genitals. Most likely, she will be frightened or confused by the incident. However, because children take their cues from grownups, she will react in the way her parents and other adults tell her to—by their own actions and attitudes.

Let's say her parents become excited and distraught over the incident. Her mother weeps. Her father calls the police in a frenzied manner. Suddenly it sweeps over the little girl that something terrible has happened to her. Until then, until her parents reacted the way they did, she had no such idea.

As a result, she can develop fears concerning sex and concerning her genital organs and the genital organs of the male, and she can have other strong feelings of guilt and of curiosity to repeat the experience to see what else might happen. Little children simply do not know how to cope with such strong feelings, so they repress them. However, we must all realize that these feelings remain buried to fester within the child, and to cause trouble later on, usually in marriage.

I do not mean to imply that parents should shrug off improper advances made toward their children. I simply plead for restraint on the part of parents in reacting to the incident while their children are present. For this is a case in which the parental "cure" can be worse than the disease.

This applies, too, when the parent finds his child reading a "dirty" book, looking at pornographic pictures, or discussing sex with his playmates. A patient had an eight-year-old daughter who delighted in locking herself and a friend into a bathroom and telling what she calls "naked stories."

I think my patient handled the situation quite well. She says: "I didn't try to create a feeling of shame in my daughter. After the friend had left, I discussed the stories with my daughter. She felt no guilt about telling me what she and her friend had talked about. I asked her if there were any questions on her mind, and I answered these in a simple manner, understandable to her.

"Most of all, I did not punish her nor create the idea in her that she was wrong, or misbehaving, or in any way different from other children of her age. But I did make it clear that she must not repeat the incident with her friend, whose mother might feel quite differently about the whole thing."

This strikes me as a singularly intelligent approach to a problem which is experienced in one form or another in almost every family. This young housewife's daughter is likely to grow up without excessive feelings in the wrong direction about sex.

I have discussed early childhood sexual experience both from the standpoint of the child and of his parents. Childhood attitudes are molded by parental attitudes. Children come to view sex and sexual difference largely through their parents' feelings and attitudes toward sex and toward each other.

Many destructive childhood attitudes can be offset, indeed prevented, if parents take an aboveboard, open, honest attitude and really communicate with their children about sex. If the information is available at home, children will seek it. They need go nowhere else. From parents we obtain our sense of social conscience and our sexual awareness, whatever its form.

Our parents did the best they could by us, according to their own standards. We will do the best we can by our children, too. Our parents made mistakes in all probability, and we, as parents, are likely to make some too.

In between, there is plenty of chance for any of us having the desire and the courage to improve on the job, especially if we keep in mind that we are bringing up not just our own children, but someone else's future husbands and wives—and the parents of our own grandchildren!

7

The Physical Aspects of Sexual Tensions

Once a centipede was racing happily along on his hundred legs when someone casually remarked, "I wonder how he knows which leg to move first?"

Instantly, the centipede began to wonder too. The question hit him hard, so hard that he was thrown into a panic. He toppled over on his back with all his hundred formerly useful legs waving wildly in the air. Never before having thought about which leg to move first, now faced with trying to decide, he found he could not move a single one.

In all the world no complex process is as incredibly smooth-running as the human body. You simply are never aware of the functioning of your various organs. Certainly most people have no idea how their intestines move their breakfast along until they have a stomach ache because the breakfast has stuck in one spot.

The miraculous functioning of the human body is possible because simultaneously there are an incredible number of electrical, chemical and physical activities going on in every tiny spot of it. The liver alone, for instance, is a great chemical factory where bile is manufactured, sugar stored, outworn blood hemoglobin destroyed, immune factors developed and toxic products rendered harmless, with a host of other complex liver functions all proceeding at the same time.

So it is with the sex organs. They are pretty much taken for granted in our consciousness until something goes wrong, or until we fear that something may go wrong. These organs, too, are a fascinating aspect of the miracle of life. To help allay anxiety concerning them, I believe everyone should know as much as possible about them.

The Female Sex Organs

In the woman, the external genital organs serve to protect internal genital structures. The external genitals also are one of the major areas of erotic response, or response to sexual excitement. Pubic hair covers the area. It is short and coarse and is one of the early signs of approaching puberty. The word *puberty* comes from *pubescent,* which means hairy. In the female, the pubic hair forms a triangle with the apex pointing down.

The External Genitals

The vulva consists of the outer labia or larger lips, the vestibule, the inner labia or smaller lips and the clitoris. The outer labia are two long, tapering tissue folds or cushions covered with hair. Their major function is to protect the delicate inner parts of the vulva.

The vestibule, a funnel-like structure, is about two inches long and can be seen when the outer labia are drawn apart. It is lined by a smooth membrane kept moist by glandular discharge. During sexual excitement, the gland ducts supply extra lubrication which permits easy entry of the penis. Also, the vestibule allows access for the tampon-type of sanitary pad, or a medical contraceptive.

The inner labia are parallel to and located on the inner part of the larger labia. They begin at the upper point of the vulva and diverge on either side like an inverted V of hanging skin folds. The inner labia are lined with nerves, blood vessels and elastic tissue. Sensitive to stimuli, they become firm and tense under sexual excitement.

Located at the upper angle of the vulva, where the two inner lips meet, is the clitoris, the external center of erotic sensation. It looks somewhat like a very tiny penis. Its tip is rounded and packed with nerve ends. The inner labia meet over the top of the clitoris to form its cover. This is called the foreskin, or prepuce, and should regularly be pulled back to allow gentle cleansing of the secretions that may collect there.

As I have said, the clitoris is extremely responsive to sexual stimuli. Because of its location and nearness to the vagina, it is sensitive to pressure and contact during sex play and in sexual relations. When the woman becomes sexually aroused, the clitoris may become erect and firm, but this may not always be obvious to the husband.

Let me tell you about two married couples I know. The first couple was experiencing unsuccessful sex relations. The wife complained that she never reached a climax and the husband began to feel that he was inadequate.

The husband, in explaining the problem to his doctor, said he had tried various techniques to stimulate his wife to the point of orgasm, but nothing succeeded.

"Have you tried stimulating the clitoris?" the doctor inquired.

"What's that?" the husband asked. "I've never heard of it."

For the first time it came to light that the husband did not know that such an organ as the clitoris existed. And, of course, he did not know anything about its importance in sexual stimulation. The doctor took out a chart of the female anatomy and explained the construction of the female genital tract.

The entire picture has changed now for the better. Not only is the husband more skillful in arousing his wife, but both husband and wife have done considerable reading about sex and have become truly literate on the subject. As a result, their sexual experience today is far more gratifying than it was in the past. In that case, one visit to the doctor resulted in one problem solved.

The second couple illustrates how knowledge can increase pleasure in sexual relations. This couple is extremely well informed. They are both mature, worldly people to whom sex is not a hidden factor in living. They think and speak of it intelligently, and look upon it as an essential part of their life together.

This couple has discovered that the wife can actually reach climax twice in a relatively short period, before and during intercourse. The husband has learned to stimulate his wife manually so that she can achieve a clitoral orgasm.

Then he inserts his penis and by tender, loving suggestion has convinced his wife that she can attain a second, or vaginal, orgasm. Much of the time, she does. Even if she does not, she already has experienced climax through stimulation of the clitoris. It goes without saying that there is relatively little sexual tension in the relations of this couple.

Incidentally, their real discovery of each other sexually came, as often happens, only after eight or nine years of marriage.

The Internal Organs

The hymen is the meeting point of the internal and external female genitals. Situated at the entrance to the vagina, it is usually shaped like a crescent. It may block the vaginal entrance completely except for a tiny opening, or it may hardly block the opening at all. Even in virgins, there is an opening in the hymen to allow the passage of menstrual discharge and other secretions. The hymen is quite elastic and in most cases there is no reason for opening it artificially before marriage. Contrary to popular belief, sports activity will rarely break or tear it.

If the hymen is intact, marital intercourse usually stretches it or breaks it. However, in some women, the hymen may remain intact for months or even years after marriage, even with frequent intercourse.

The vagina is the canal which extends from the vulva inward. Into it is inserted the penis during intercourse, and down through it will pass the baby at birth. During sexual excitement, the vagina is lubricated by fluid produced by two tiny glands. Fluid volume increases as stimulation increases. In the virgin, the vagina measures about a half-inch in diameter. After marriage and childbirth, the diameter increases to one and a half or two inches. The vagina is about three or three and one-half inches long and the cervix, or neck of the womb, projects into it at its upper end. Its walls are very elastic so that it can expand easily to receive the penis. The floor is formed by several bands of muscle covered with smooth mucous membrane. It is the involuntary but regular spasm of contractions in these muscular bands that constitutes the orgasm or climax in the woman.

The uterus, or womb, is a pear-shaped organ usually two and

a half to three and a half inches long and two inches or so wide. Its thick, muscular walls surround a cavity that has three openings. The lower one, tightly closed except during birth, leads through the cervix to the vagina, the two on top lead to the Fallopian tubes. Lined with a special membrane, the cavity undergoes dynamic changes monthly as part of menstruation. It is here that the egg, or ovum, enters through the Fallopian tubes from the ovaries.

The ovaries are the two female sex glands which are similar to the testes of the male. They are located in the lower part of the abdomen on each side of the uterus. Each resembles a large, flattened olive in shape and size. The ovaries not only develop the female germ cells, but as tiny chemical factories, they also produce two sex hormones.

The "ripening" process of the eggs begins with the onset of puberty. In each menstrual cycle (28 days is the usual time period for a cycle, although there is great, normal variation), only one egg usually matures. If two ova are discharged and fertilized, non-identical twins result. Identical twins come from a single fertilized ovum that splits into two. The moment of discharge of the ovum from the ovary is called ovulation, and it generally takes place about fourteen days before the onset of the next menstrual cycle. At ovulation, some women experience slight cramps similar to those of menstruation, or slight staining. These women are fortunate in being able to tell exactly when they ovulate.

The mature egg finds its way from the ovary into one of the Fallopian tubes, each of which is about five inches long, and travels down it, slowly making its way toward the uterus. It is usually in the tube that the sperm fertilizes the egg. If it remains unfertilized, it is simply expelled with the menstrual flow which begins at this time. If fertilization of the egg has taken place, the tiny being already developing into an embryo implants itself in the lining of the uterus which has become thick and velvety in preparation for it. Pregnancy is considered by scientists to have begun at the moment of fertilization.

Ovulation ceases until the pregnancy is over, as does menstruation, although, occasionally, staining may occur at the usual time of the period. This staining may take place for only a short while during pregnancy, or occasionally for longer.

The Male Organs

The penis is suspended from the bony part of the pelvis and its major functions are to discharge urine from the bladder and to deposit the seminal fluid in the female genital tract. It consists of a body and head (glans). The glans, as in the clitoris, is covered with a prepuce or foreskin which is removed when a circumcision is performed. This foreskin, too, should be pushed back regularly for thorough cleansing.

The penis, extremely sensitive to the touch, hangs loosely in front of the scrotum, a pouch which holds the testes. When not erect, the penis is about three and a half inches long, although here again, there is a great range of normal variation. When it becomes rigid during erection, of course, its length and thickness increase considerably.

Most of the seminal fluid consists of secretions from the sex glands, the prostate and the seminal vesicles. The important element in the seminal fluid is sperm, or spermatozoa, of which there are normally two hundred million in the teaspoon of seminal fluid ejaculated at each intercourse.

The testes are male sex glands oval in shape, about one and a half inches long and one inch thick. They are contained in the scrotum. The sperm travels from the testes toward the penis through a long coiled tube called the epididymis, which lies alongside the testes. In the epididymis, spermatozoa undergo a gradual process of maturation. This tube becomes the spermatic duct, or vas, which curves upward in the scrotum and, passing behind the bladder, leads into the urethra. The seminal vesicles are connected with it, and produce a gelatinlike secretion which mixes with the spermatozoa as they pass into the urethra at ejaculation.

The prostate, a gland shaped somewhat like a horse chestnut, is located in front of the rectum and below the bladder, and surrounds the urethra to which it is connected by a duct. When ejaculation occurs, the prostate contracts and adds to the seminal fluid its own milky secretion. The exact function of this secretion is not fully understood, but it is believed that it contains a substance which helps to liquefy the gelatinous semen after ejaculation.

Under the microscope, spermatozoa look like tiny tadpoles, consisting of a head, middle section and tail. In the head and middle section are the chromosomes and genes which determine the characteristics of the child that are inherited from the father. A sperm cell travels about an inch in eight minutes in the female genital tract in search of the mature egg cell.

Pain in Intercourse

There may be slight physical pain for the woman at the outset of marriage. However, this usually subsides in a short time. I say usually. By that I mean in the overwhelming percentage of cases. Very often, when women complain of pain long after they are married, this may be due to an unnoticed chronic infection which yields readily to treatment. If there is no infection, then the pain may have a psychic rather than a physical basis. The woman may quite simply not enjoy intercourse. Without enjoyment, the muscles surrounding the vagina not only do not relax, but may even go into spasm. Penetration by the penis against such spasm can be intensely painful.

I would urge such a woman to have a physical checkup. If nothing of importance is detected, the next step for such a woman is to seek, with the help of a competent therapist, an emotional basis for her problem.

I know a woman who experienced this type of muscular contraction or genital spasm. When she finally sought help, her emotional difficulties came clearly into focus, and she admitted to herself that she was afraid to have intercourse for two reasons. First, she feared childbirth, and second, she feared that if she used a contraceptive she would develop cancer.

Painstaking explanation of the facts plus emotional support by her physician finally convinced her that she could face pregnancy without fear when she was ready for it. She also accepted his reassurance that modern medical contraceptives as listed by the American Medical Association have not been found to cause cancer.

Genital Organ Disproportion

This accounts for such a very minor number of sexual failures among married couples that I believe this fact needs re-emphasizing. I know of wives who are so convinced that their husbands' penises are oversized that they are wary of intercourse. This has led to unhappy times for these couples. The fact of the matter is that few husbands and wives are mismated organically, if for no other reason than that most of the people in this country have genital development falling within the normal size range. Furthermore, women should remember that the vagina is capable of great stretching—even to being able to accommodate the passage of an eight- to ten-pound baby!

Climax and Conception

As I've mentioned, males reach the point of climax more readily than females. One wife I spoke to not long ago believed that conception could not take place unless she too reached climax. And, the wife added, if the woman does not often reach climax, there must be something physically wrong. Both notions are false. If conception could not take place without the woman reaching climax, there would be no pregnancies as the result of rape. As for the second notion, that climax is an index of physical well-being, there is no evidence that it is so. It takes time for most women to reach climax as easily or as often as their husbands do. There is some evidence that at least a few women do not even desire to reach climax each time there is coitus.

Physical Comfort in Intercourse

One cause of sexual tension is physical discomfort during intercourse. Certainly this is a mechanical factor that can be ironed out by an understanding husband and wife, but it is quite common. Either mate does something in intercourse that is physically painful and this is the source of tension. It might be the position of the body, the placement of an arm or a leg, distribution of part or all of body weight.

At times, too, the man or his wife may indulge in some sort of exercise or leisure-time pursuit that causes physical stress in the lower portion of the body. A woman I know found that she could not bear intercourse for some appreciable time after horseback riding. Knowing this, she has adjusted her leisure habits somewhat.

In general, both husband and wife should learn the basics of physical comfort in intercourse. Lights, covers, room temperatures, size of bed—all should be adjusted for greatest comfort. A certain amount of attention should be paid to position, but it should not be unduly emphasized. Although it is thought to be a key factor in marital love, the fact is that it is not.

The Impotent Male

A great deal has been said and written about the infertile male, much of it more than a little erroneous. It has been found by exhaustive studies that five percent or fewer of all married men are infertile, with sperm counts too low to allow conception to take place.

Infertility does not mean impotence. Even if a man is infertile, he usually is entirely potent, that is, capable of normal intercourse. Infertility need bear no relationship to male genital size, sexual desire or potency.

Impotence in the male is a special subject in itself, and in nearly every case the cause is psychic. The man who suffers from impotence should seek psychiatric help.

Strength of Sexual Desire

Many people believe that gradations of sexual desire are controlled by physical factors only. Thus, a woman once said to me, "That young teen-ager is oversexed—her glands are the reason." Or a young executive said not long ago, "I'm rather neutral about sex. I guess I'm underdeveloped physically." Let me emphasize that physical factors as they relate to sexual desire are rare indeed. If an individual has great sex desires or less, the differential is almost always psychological and is caused by upbringing, teaching and experience. Furthermore, sexual desire shows considerable variation in the same individual at different times.

Here, perhaps more than in any other area, we are creatures of our conditioning. It is not possible to construct an exact pattern of upbringing sure to result in increased or decreased desire. However, if the child is brought up in a home atmosphere of love and free expression of affection, and with freedom to communicate with his parents about his innermost thoughts and feelings concerning sex, he is less likely to grow up unable to achieve mature love expression in his marriage.

Many people believe that in marriage the cardinal problem is an imbalance between the desire for sex on the part of the husband and of the wife. Usually we hear that men desire sex more often than women and that this throws marital sex out of kilter. True, this does occur. However, very little is said about wives who desire sex more often than their husbands. This also occurs and we will discuss it later on.

This brings us to still another vital point. Many people are unclear on the subject of sex as a release for physical tensions. Does sex really provide such a release?

The Role of Sex in Physical Tensions

As I have said, sex organs are much like other organs in the body, relatively unobtrusive until they make their needs known. The urinary bladder and the rectum, for instance, make their needs known when they must discharge body wastes. Similarly, signals are transmitted to the brain from the sex organs informing us of the need for discharge of sexual tension. The actual causes of this tension are not clear, but that it does exist cannot be denied.

The first manifestation of this in the male is at puberty when boys begin having what are commonly referred to as "wet dreams," when during sleep there is an automatic discharge of semen. This may or may not be accompanied by a dream in which the boy feels a pleasurable sensation at the time of discharge. Girls rarely have this type of dream, at least not as regularly and automatically as boys do.

Another form of release of tension in both male and female is masturbation. I talked about this before and indicated that almost every human being had quite normally masturbated at some time in his or her life. I also said that the most harmful effect of masturbation is the sense of guilt that may accompany it.

There are certain religious groups to whom masturbation is definitely sinful. Persons of these faiths should most certainly seek the advice of their religious counselors concerning this matter. Persons of the faiths which do not look upon masturbation as a sin should still not hesitate to seek counsel if masturbation becomes a problem to them. In any case, I cannot emphasize too strongly that *it is not physically harmful.* Furthermore, no one can honestly deny that it does release sexual tension.

The Changing Social Picture

Animals during their mating season provide prime examples of sexual tension. A male stag during the rutting season will run for miles seeking a female to court. For human beings, there are no such seasons. Powerful sexual drives are likely to hit and hit hard during that period following puberty when our young people are still in a stage of immaturity and financial dependency.

This is one of the prices we pay for living in our civilization. Unlike most primitive cultures where the age of sexual maturity more or less coincides with the age at which it is permissible to undertake sexual relationships, our civilization points its finger sternly and says, "No, you may not have sexual intercourse until you are married. And you may not marry until you are able to support a family by your own efforts."

A big change in this chain of prohibitions, however, has come about since the Second World War. Suddenly, young people are marrying earlier and earlier. They are continuing their schooling not only in marriage, but actually while having their families. Most of these young marriages that continue with the education of one or both partners are supported partially or wholly by one or both sets of parents.

Premarital Intercourse

The powerful sexual drives which reach their peaks between the ages of seventeen and twenty-two in males, and somewhat later in females, have caused changes in cultural patterns in other ways. It is useless to blink at the fact that premarital sexual intercourse has increased greatly.

In one study, about 40 percent of all college women interviewed indicated that they had already had intercourse before marriage or would not balk at it in the future. In another study, more than 50 percent of high school and college boys said they had already had intercourse or hoped to.

Teen-agers have become less and less inhibited in this regard. Not long ago, a friend told me that her fifteen-year-old daughter had announced, "I plan to learn about sex before marriage. I know you won't like this, but I want to have intercourse before I'm married."

How should the parent react? If she registers shock and criticism, she sets up a climate of hostility that may interrupt further communication with her daughter. If she blinks at the announcement and passes it off lightly, the parent courts the real danger of making her daughter feel that her mother does not care about her welfare.

The sane course, I believe, is to continue the discussion on a person-to-person basis with the daughter. The wastefulness and danger of promiscuous intercourse "as a lark" or "as an experience" should be stressed. So should the fact that the best kind of intercourse is achieved when carried out with one beloved person, your spouse, through life. The meaningfulness of intercourse when it is an expression of love must be defined for the teen-ager, who tends to equate sex with love.

The parent should discuss the unhappy consequences of premarital sex, the most serious of which, I think, is disillusionment. I believe the greatest defeat suffered by the teen-ager who insists on premarital sex is an emotional one. For, almost invariably, the young person finds that something was missing—true, abiding love, which he or she is as yet too young to recognize and define. The parent must stress, too, other consequences of premarital sex, such as babies born out of wedlock and venereal disease.

Babies Out of Wedlock

The rate of illegitimacy has skyrocketed in the past decade. As a matter of fact, the United States Children's Bureau has stated that the illegitimacy rate among girls aged thirteen to seventeen increased by 40 percent in the decade 1946–56.

For every girl who "got caught," and bore a child out of wedlock, there must have been a fair number who "got away with it." Certainly, conversations with young people in high school and college reveal—with a frankness unheard-of before World War II—the extent to which premarital sexual relations are practiced.

Venereal disease rates, especially among young, unmarried people, are up alarmingly in many locales in the United States.

Indeed, there have even been some epidemics of venereal disease among teen-agers in certain communities. New cases are occurring at a rate not of thousands per year, but of hundreds of thousands. These are the known cases. However, many are unreported, which leads some public health authorities to estimate the new case load at over a million per year.

It must be obvious, therefore, that threats about babies out of wedlock or venereal disease have not served as deterrents to teen-age premarital sex experience. Something else must be offered if the youngster is really to understand the ramifications of sex before and after marriage. That something else, I believe, must come from a lifetime of conditioning in a home where parental authority is respected rather than feared, and where religious and ethical ideals have been practiced daily rather than just on the Sabbath. The aim is in-built controls in the young person, to make up for the rapid disappearance of outer controls.

Must Sexual Energy Be Used?

Many people persuade themselves that sexual tensions are an excuse for indulging in premarital sexual intercourse. However, it is not true that a man, or a woman for that matter, would become ill if his sexual energy were not released periodically. It is dishonest to use this "excuse" for promiscuity. For most people, continence can be a perfectly healthy state. The question of whether to "give in" or "be strong" will be resolved by the individual on the basis of his own character and ideals. The decision will depend, too, on whether he willingly uses another person as a tool for his own satisfaction, or is able to hold his desires in check until he has found a true partner in the full sense of the word—and for life.

Sex As Expression

Not many people have stopped to consider that sex organs are organs of expression—just as are the hands, the eyes, the voice, the entire body. Stop and think about it a moment. The way you use your sexual powers depends a great deal on how you feel about life in general.

We have mentioned those who use sex as a weapon, as a club. Then there is the man who is secretly unsure of himself. He is likely to use sex in an overaggressive fashion. He has a drive to subjugate sexually as many women as possible, in order to prove how virile and successful he is. He certainly is not expressing love with each of these women. In fact, he may not be capable of expressing love at all.

Correspondingly there are those women who are mature sexually, but immature emotionally. These women carry their sexuality about like a torch, trying to arouse all those whom they meet. But most often it is a torch without fire. These women have nothing with which to back up the provocative façade, and they are actually unable, very often, to carry through their hothouse sexual claims. These are women who are expressing deep insecurity about their own inability to carry out the female role, and their attempt to subjugate every man they meet is really an attempt to prove their femininity.

There are other types: the wife or husband who uses sex as a bargaining weapon; the individual who refuses to recognize the existence of sex; the person whose dress either is intended to provoke or to deny sex; the person who sits, stands, moves in such a way as to emphasize or de-emphasize sex.

It should be remembered that the American culture is one in which a high premium is placed on sex, suggestion and the muted half-note of sexual desire. The auto advertisement rarely appears without a pretty girl somewhere in the picture. The implication: buy the car and a girl like this one will be part of the deal. Our films, our ads, our clothing, our social conditioning are lathered generously with sex. So if you wish to see how falsely sex can be expressed, just look around you.

Another Anxiety Causing Sexual Tensions

Actually, there are few if any physical conditions that would, in themselves, cause sexual tension. There are many fears or worries about real or imagined physical conditions, however, that certainly can cause sexual tension.

There is one form of anxiety, usually occurring early in marriage, which merits attention. At times, a wife who has masturbated prior to marriage feels a sense of devastating disappointment because the sexual act is not as pleasurable to her as masturbation was. Few women will admit this or talk about it. Probably the innate sense of guilt and shame prevents open recognition of the fact that at one time or another they provided themselves with a certain amount of physical pleasure.

However, if such women could once face this honestly, the situation would resolve itself. First of all, such women should realize that in masturbation only one person with one set of feelings is involved, and that person knows exactly how to evoke the feeling that she seeks.

Now, in the new relationship of marriage, she must wait for a comparative stranger, her husband, to learn how to evoke the feeling that she is already so skillful at evoking for herself. Usually, she is torn between a desire to show him or tell him how, and a sense of disappointment at his seeming ineptitude. Mixed with these strong emotions is a sense of guilt and a natural shyness. Together, these make her unable to tell her husband how she feels, and the result is a sense of complete frustration over the whole experience.

What happens ultimately in this situation? Gradually, the wife learns to train her feelings so that her husband's efforts can succeed in evoking what she formerly provided for herself. If communication were better than it usually is between husband and wife, this process could easily be shortened, for she then could indicate to him what he could do to give her pleasure. Unfortunately, it may take years for a husband and wife to learn to talk to each other about such intimate things as their own sexual feelings, and some never do learn.

Demands in Married Love

Tensions are bound to arise, too, when one of the partners wishes to do something or have something done in sex play or intercourse which the other finds shocking, distasteful or abhorrent. This situation can lead to serious consequences. Recently, I received a letter from the distraught father of a young married man. He wrote that the marriage was moving quickly toward divorce because his son insisted on certain types of sex play which the young wife found "immoral." I felt extremely sorry for the people in this situation, one so unnecessary. It is not an easy matter to deal with through correspondence, but after suggesting a number of books for the young couple to read, and the names of some marriage counselors in their vicinity, I ended my letter as follows:

"It would be extremely helpful if your son's wife could achieve the understanding that there are as many ways of loving as there are people in the world; that no way of expressing love is bad in itself, nor can it be harmful.

"Our upbringing, particularly in regard to girls, is such that we are handicapped. We are taught to contain our emotions and to look upon them with almost total restraint until the great moment of the wedding night. Then we are supposed to free ourselves completely from our inhibitions. This simply is not possible.

"I hope that your son can be helped to understand the need for patience here. I hope, too, that he and his wife together can proceed slowly, exploring little by little the various ways there are for expressing mutual love. A year from now, she will probably be amused to remember how she felt a year previously. Even then, she may not be ready to comply fully with your son's wishes, but I believe she would surely find that she was far more ready for experimentation in physical love than she was a year ago. And your son might begin to understand that it is not necessary to seek all the ways of enjoying sex at once. He might begin to realize that it pays to savor them slowly. A couple can discover these ways together one at a time over a period of one year, five, ten—even thirty years or longer.

"And thus it could proceed, with slow and steady progress, if they can only trust each other and feel that any way of expressing love to each other is a good and a proper way. . . ."

Indeed, there is one great truism that I wish everyone, particularly wives, could learn. It is that sex in itself, with a person whom you love and who loves you, is good, and nothing you do in this relationship could possibly be wrong.

It is in a relationship of true permanence and security in marriage that husbands and wives can come to feel this way about marital sex and all that goes with it. Only when you feel secure and safe in your love and the love of your partner can you freely let yourself go to express that which your body was meant to express.

To sum up, there *are* physical factors in sexual anxiety but most of them are temporary or exist only because of emotional attitudes. Most sources of sexual tension can be overcome. The complete freedom and security of marriage which fosters sexual fulfillment develops with time, with honesty and with an all-pervasive sincerity, and with the firm belief that sex with the person you love is very, very good.

The results are well worth the investment of several decades of our lives.

8

Fear As a Cause of Sexual Tensions

Fear and suspicion are among the most destructive feelings we have. Sometimes it is difficult to distinguish one from the other, for they usually are closely intertwined.

I am not talking particularly about fear of the marriage partner. Rather, I am talking about the feeling of fear as it applies in many phases of our lives. Nowhere is fear more capable of interfering than in the sexual relationship.

I shall discuss four types of fear which are common in regard to sexual behavior in marriage. Each is typical of similar fears expressed repeatedly in the doctor's office and in cases heard by marriage counselors and by religious advisors. *These examples of fears are: fear of being overheard; fear of giving oneself completely in the sex act; fear of pregnancy and fear of infidelity.*

Fear of Being Overheard

I suppose that among men this is a minor consideration, or even possibly a stimulant, but there is no question that among women, the very thought that someone might overhear during sex play or the sex act itself is enough to drive all sexual feeling far, far away.

It is reassuring to know that this kind of fear is likely to be only temporarily destructive. However, in a marriage that is already vulnerable, there can be serious consequences. I recall the case of a young couple who were guests at the country home of a friend.

Many houses are not constructed as solidly as they might be. On the first night, the wife refused to have intercourse because, she said, "the walls are too thin." This dismayed the husband, but he complied. On the second night, he had convinced her that no one would overhear. Or at least, he thought he had.

During intercourse itself, with its special motions, rhythms and sounds from husband and wife, the wife suddenly sat bolt upright in bed.

"We're making too much noise," she said in a stage whisper.

"We are *not*," the husband said, in loud disgruntled tones.

Then there ensued an argument, which increased in intensity as it proceeded. The host and hostess *did* overhear the argument, although they had heard nothing beforehand. The couple brooded for the rest of the visit and had a miserable time and, needless to say, no sex.

Now, such a temporary dislocation of emotions would have little effect on a solid marriage. This one was not solid, however.

The husband and wife never had made a good adjustment to each other and the episode was simply another straw added to the camel's back. Later on, that couple separated for several months. Fortunately, they consulted a marriage counselor and are back together once again. As yet, the marriage is still not out of danger. It will take some time for the couple to work out their problems, among which the sexual aspect looms large.

The examples of fear of being overheard could themselves fill a book. I know of a couple who live in a sprawling apartment project in which the walls are not too thick. In the quiet of the late evening, you can actually hear the people talking next door. In bed, these muffled voices sounded to the wife as if someone actually were in the room. When she heard the voices, she refused to have intercourse.

This disturbed her husband from time to time and finally they had a frank, open discussion of it. "I feel as if our neighbors are in the bedroom with us," she said. "That's why I act the way I do."

For some weeks, the husband and wife discussed this little quirk of hers, and finally they worked it out by playing soft radio music to mask the voices, but mostly by laughing at the whole thing. Fortunately, the wife's sense of humor prevailed in the end.

Another couple told me that they had never had intercourse when they stayed overnight in a motel because of the wife's fear of being overheard, so recently, they have stopped in hotels. Her fear has dissolved. It sounds simple and it is simple. Very often the source of sexual tension will diminish in importance as a result of some such simple act on the part of one or both partners. This can be true in almost any case of tension caused by superficial reasons, and there are a great many of those.

Another couple encountered trouble when, on several occasions just as they were about to have intercourse, the phone rang. "I've completely lost my desire," the wife would announce, when her husband returned from the phone. "Don't ask me to tell you why. That's just the way I am."

The unhappy husband gave the matter a little thought. Take the phone out of the bedroom, put it in another room, tone down the bell, and let it ring its fool head off, he said to himself. Simple, you may think, a little mechanical thing, but it worked. One point: countless tensions in marital sexuality will yield to even-tempered, well-considered thinking. A second point: they will not yield if the situation is being used as an excuse to avoid intercourse.

Fear of Giving Oneself Completely

This is a deeper kind of fear than that discussed in the previous case. This fear involves a feeling that if you give yourself totally in every phase of the relationship as well as the sexual one, you may lose your identity as a whole person. I suspect this fear is much more common among women than among men.

Obviously, this kind of fear is related to suspicion, distrust and perhaps to ulterior motives. It probably stems from a feeling of lack of safety in the other person, a feeling of being threatened. I recall a young wife who once said to her doctor: "I never allow myself to be so carried away in intercourse that I approach the point of orgasm. I would not be able to control myself, I'm sure. I'm afraid to face myself in this kind of primitive situation, or to let my husband see me so uncontrolled."

What a tragic attitude! Of course, this woman needed medical counseling. Her remarks reveal a great deal about herself. Perhaps the most interesting thing they reveal is that she lacks genuine faith in herself as well as in her husband. She lacks ability really to participate not only in marital sex but in any intimate relationship. Obviously, if she remains unchanged, she will make herself and her husband miserable.

Certainly, the attitude, "I refuse to give myself completely," is not a sound basis for marriage. How to handle it? That's the key question.

Overcoming the Fear

First, you must take a good look at your partner. You must determine whether your partner is such a questionable and untrustworthy person that you cannot trust your own reactions in his presence. You must seek to determine, honestly and forthrightly, whether your lack of faith in your partner is real, imagined, or an excuse.

If you do this, and I mean really do it, not just go through the motions, I think you will often be surprised. A good deal of the time you will be startled to discover that your partner might also have misgivings and fears concerning *your* reactions.

What a strange situation! Here are two adults, married (mature?), people playing a game which leads to stress and emotional pain. "I'll trust you," each seems to say to the other, "if you will trust me. But I cannot start trusting you until you start trusting me. *You* make the first gesture, then I can make the next gesture." And so the merry-go-round goes.

The mature, grown-up way is to discuss the problem between you. Put your cards on the table. Don't be content to play what can become a dangerous charade.

Some people will say it is religious sentimentality to suggest that in order to receive trust, one must first feel trust. I doubt it. Somebody must make the first gesture. And in marriage, making that first gesture can be extremely important. Marriage is the best investment we can make in life and there is no investment possible without some element of risk.

If everyone played safe in their human-relations investments, nobody would ever take the first step in expressing and showing trust. Having picked a mate, with heart, mind and sexual feelings, the hand of friendship should be extended as well as the kiss of love. Can't husband and wife be true friends as well as lovers? And true friendship implies trust.

Fear of Pregnancy

This is still another prevalent fear that can work havoc with the marriage relationship. I shall not forget the young wife who told me: "I'm determined not to become pregnant, I'm too afraid of having a baby. Maybe I'll change in the future, but that's how I feel now. I won't let my husband come close to me except on certain days I think are safe based on my menstrual cycle."

Here was a cool, calculating, but nevertheless fear-ridden woman who was destroying the spontaneity of her marriage. For some time, the wife clung to her unreasoning fear. Then, finally, she became pregnant. Her fear intensified. On her first visit to the obstetrician, she was trembling. For more than an hour, the doctor comforted her, reassured her that the chances were overwhelmingly against any mishap occurring.

After some probing, he discovered the two-sided basis of his patient's fear. First, she felt that she would die in childbirth. Second, she believed she might give birth to an "imperfect" child. These, incidentally, are the two most common fears in pregnancy.

I take my hat off to that obstetrician. He did what I am afraid is not often enough done in such cases. He spent much extra time during her regular monthly appointment periods—and at certain times in between—explaining how safe childbirth is nowadays for both mother and baby.

After five months, he finally convinced her that there was

only the remotest possibility of anything being wrong with the baby and that she would come through it all with flying colors—as indeed she did. In the meantime, since she was pregnant already, her fear of intercourse disappeared, to her own and her husband's great satisfaction.

Another woman, aged thirty and married five years, was extremely afraid of pregnancy, but for another prevalent reason. She was afraid that pregnancy would permanently distort her body and destroy her beauty. She had convinced herself that pregnancy would mean loss of her appeal to her husband and, ultimately, divorce.

She expressed this fear to a close friend who put her in touch with a patient and considerate doctor. Together, this woman and the doctor worked out the problem. He explained the facts about weight gain to the woman—that the pounds can roll off after the birth of a child—and the woman softened in her fear of pregnancy. After some considerable time, she became convinced that pregnancy would not turn her into a grotesque individual. Later, she became pregnant and discovered for herself the truth of the doctor's words.

It goes without saying that fear of pain is one of the most universal fears. One woman I know had such a fear and she dreaded the thought of becoming pregnant. As a result of her dread, she permitted herself and her husband to have intercourse very infrequently. This, of course, was the source of considerable tension in their household.

Luckily, this wife had gone to school with a woman who had become a registered nurse. They renewed their friendship and the wife expressed her fear to the nurse. The latter explained the uses of modern anesthesia in the labor and delivery room and the wife's fear decreased to the point where normal sex relations and pregnancy followed naturally and easily.

Today, she has three children. If you ask her about pain in childbirth, her reply is: "Of course, it's not painless, but for goodness' sake, anyone can take some discomfort once in a while."

The cases above illustrate fear of pregnancy where fear should not really exist. Let's turn to such fears as may be justified. Fear can exist, understandably, where health or economic circumstances of the couple are such that an additional pregnancy would cause real harm.

Consider the wife who has had a really difficult time with her first two pregnancies and has since developed diabetes. She has been cautioned by her doctor not to become pregnant for some time. He points out, and rightly, that a "quick" pregnancy might prove deleterious to her health and to the equilibrium of the entire family. It would be quite normal for such a wife to be unable to respond to her husband completely because of the devastating fear of pregnancy.

Or consider the wife of a laborer who already has three children and who knows full well that her husband brings home only $60 a week or so in his pay envelope. She, too, might have a justifiable fear of pregnancy. Already, this wife is struggling to stretch her meager table allowance to meet the family needs. In this era of high prices and inflation, she is likely to be despondent about her entire economic and family status.

Contraception—the Answer

Modern medicine has made it possible for married couples in every circumstance and every walk of life to continue deepening their marital relationships by expressing mutual love without fear of pregnancy. Contraception is the answer.

Even among Roman Catholics, the only group that does not accept medical contraception, the rhythm method, if practiced with extreme care under the guidance of a knowledgeable physician, can, in most cases, permit the couple to plan pregnancies quite successfully.

Until recently there was a tendency on the part of a few

religious groups to hold that the primary purpose of marriage was procreation, and that therefore the sexual act should not be indulged in except for this purpose. Most of the large religious groups have now turned from this belief. Perhaps the best statement of the newer thinking on the part of a religious body is embodied in the resolutions and conclusions of the Lambeth Conference held in England in 1958. This was sponsored by the Anglican (Episcopal) Church with a total of forty-six nations represented. The Conference findings in regard to family planning resulted from years of study and discussion. Here are a few excerpts from Conference conclusions:

". . . The Conference believes that the responsibility for deciding upon the number and frequency of children has been laid by God upon the consciences of parents everywhere; that this planning, in such ways as are mutually acceptable to husband and wife in Christian conscience, is a right and important factor in Christian family life and should be the result of positive choice before God. . . ."

"The process of human reproduction, from the earliest levels of Biblical revelation, has been seen as invested with a special and responsible dignity.

"The Biblical revelation, however, does not limit the function of sexuality and the family to the reproductive purpose. . . ."

"It has been common in Christian theology to mention the procreative function first, as if to say that it is the ruling purpose. But it is clearly not true that all other duties and relationships in marriage must be subordinate to the procreative one. . . ."

"The responsible procreation of children is a primary obligation. The questions, How many children? At what intervals?

are matters on which no general counsel can be given. The choice must be made by parents together, in prayerful consideration of their resources, the society in which they live, and the problems they face. . . ."

"It may be said, however, that responsible parenthood implies a watchful guard against selfishness and covetousness and an equally thoughtful awareness of the world into which our children are to be born. . . ."

"The *means* of family planning are in large measure matters of clinical and aesthetic choice, subject to the requirement that they be admissible to the Christian conscience. Scientific studies can rightly help, and do, in assessing the effects and the usefulness of any particular means; and Christians have every right to use the gifts of science for proper ends. . . ."

I might add here a previous statement made by the Augustana Lutheran Church at its 95th Synod. It says in part: "The means which a married couple uses to determine the numbers and the spacing of the births of their children are a matter for them to decide with their own consciences, on the basis of competent medical advice and in a sense of accountability to God . . ."

In May, 1959, the United Presbyterian Church stated that "proper use of medically approved contraceptives may contribute to the spiritual, emotional and economic welfare of the family."

It is significant indeed that such unequivocal statements now are coming from religious denominations representing millions upon millions of adherents throughout the world. In essence, such statements proclaim that sex in marriage is good in and of itself, co-equally good with procreation.

Religious groups have also acknowledged that modern medical methods are appropriate to prevent population growth from stifling the world. Fortunately, death rates have decreased so that it is no longer necessary for couples to have four, five and six children to sustain nations. It is entirely possible for populations to remain constant if families have only two children.

The Time for Contraception

Because people are marrying younger than ever and having their children early in married life, many families consider themselves completed before the parents reach the age of thirty. There is nothing to prevent having children past the parental age of thirty, but if a young couple decides that the family *is* complete, there stretches ahead a very long period of life together, perhaps twenty years, when the woman is still perfectly capable of becoming pregnant.

What a pity if for those twenty years the couple's love relationship were always to be shadowed by the fear of pregnancy. Some of the most moving letters I have received are those from wives who love their husbands deeply. Often, they have been unable to respond in years past to their husbands because of a deep-seated fear of additional pregnancies which they know they would be unable to accept, either because of ill health or because of poverty.

They adored the children they already had, but they simply could not face additional children. The gratitude of these women is tremendous when they are given access to modern medical methods for controlling their pregnancies. They feel completely liberated. For the first time in years, or perhaps for the first time ever, they can be free to respond to their husbands.

The same is true for young couples who have had three or four children at rapid intervals. Deeply in love, they may be afraid of sex because they desperately need time before the next baby—time to be free of sleepless nights, formulas, diapers, time to enjoy the babyhood and young childhood of the children they have, time to rediscover each other as lovers. Later, rested and fresh, they may decide to add to their family —deliberately and with the utmost joy and anticipation.

Information concerning contraception (birth control) can be obtained from most physicians. In addition, such information is available in Planned Parenthood centers throughout the United States and in the obstetrical services of almost all American medical schools. Marriage counselors and clergymen can be helpful in directing young couples to sources of information.

Contraceptive Methods

The following are listed roughly in the order of their reliability.

1. Diaphragm and Jelly. A diaphragm is an absolutely harmless device made of soft rubber with a flexible metal spring around the circumference. The diaphragm is placed in the vagina. Its purpose is to cover the cervix, which is the entrance to the uterus. Before obtaining a diaphragm, each individual woman must be examined by a physician. Only then can the diaphragm be properly fitted because the required size and shape vary from individual to individual.

Along with the diaphragm, a contraceptive jelly or cream must always be used. One of the great advantages of the diaphragm is that it may be inserted as much as an hour before intercourse; it should always be left in place for at least six hours afterward. Douching is not at all necessary. However, if the woman wishes, she may douche with plain warm water before and after removing the diaphragm. The physician who fits the diaphragm will give detailed instructions for its proper use.

2. *The Condom.* The diaphragm, previously described, is used by the wife. Just as effective is the condom, or rubber, which can be used by the husband to cover the penis. It is put on just before the sex act and captures the seminal fluid, which thus does not reach the female generative organs. The condom is harmless. There is, however, always the possibility that it may break before or during intercourse, or slip off, enabling semen to spill into the vagina. For more complete protection, therefore, it is desirable that the wife also insert some contraceptive jelly or cream into the vagina before intercourse.

3. *Jellies and Creams Alone.* Some brands of jellies and creams are designed to be used alone. A special applicator comes with each tube and is required to introduce the cream or jelly product into the vagina. They are very effective as contraceptives, but they are probably even more so when used with the diaphragm or condom. If intercourse is repeated, another dose of jelly or cream must be inserted each time. No douche is necessary, but if one is desired, it should not be taken until at least six hours after the last intercourse. This gives the product time to have its effect on the sperm.

4. *Foaming Vaginal Tablet.* When this dry tablet is slightly moistened with saliva or water and placed deep in the vagina five minutes before each intercourse, a chemical foam is generated which is inimical to sperm cells. The tablet sometimes causes a slight feeling of warmth when it foams, but it is harmless and produces no after-effects. Whenever intercourse is repeated, an additional tablet should be inserted. No douche should be taken until six hours after the last intercourse. The

foam tablet, like the cream or jelly alone, has not yet been proved to be as reliable as the diaphragm and jelly combined. The simpler methods are so much easier to use, however, that for some couples they are very much more acceptable.

5. *Suppositories.* These are small cones or capsules containing sperm-destroying chemicals in a base of cocoa butter or other substances that melt at body temperature. They are inserted into the vagina five minutes before intercourse, where they melt gradually. As they do so, a barrier is set up between sperm cells and the uterus. Suppositories definitely are not as effective as the previously described methods.

6. *Experimental Pills.* In the past few years, contraceptive pills to be taken by mouth have been introduced. They are still in the experimental stage and are dispensed by prescription only. The woman usually takes one pill a day from the fifth day on after the start of her menstrual period. She continues taking a pill daily through the twenty-fifth day of the cycle. Two or three days later, there is bleeding, which marks the beginning of a new cycle.

Three Methods Not Recommended by Doctors

The following are unsatisfactory, ineffective, or even dangerous.

1. *Penis Withdrawal.* This also is called coitus interruptus, or "taking care." The male withdraws his penis from the female genital canal just before ejaculation. This method is not recommended because it may not be possible for the male to withdraw in time. More important, even if he does, both he and his wife may soon discover that the desired spontaneity and satisfaction of marital sex are greatly decreased. Coitus inter-

ruptus may thus create emotional problems, anxieties and fears when it is used regularly. However, for occasional or emergency use, it is very effective.

2. *The Douche*. The douche alone is totally unreliable. Don't use it for protection against pregnancy.

3. *Devices for Inside the Cervix or Uterus.* Gynecologists in the United States do not approve of these at all.

Thus, we have seen that there are a variety of contraceptive methods, some more reliable than others. In addition, we have seen that the entire concept of child-spacing and family-size control is endorsed whole-heartedly by all religious bodies, with full acceptance of medical methods by all but the Roman Catholic Church.

The Rhythm Method

This method is based on the woman's so-called "safe period," safe, that is, from the standpoint of conception. A woman usually ovulates about fourteen days before the first day of each menstruation. Allowing for variables in sperm and egg life and in length of cycle (26 to 31 days), a woman's "fertile period" falls between the eleventh and the nineteenth days after the beginning of menstruation. Intercourse should be avoided during these days. Exact calculation of "safe days" should not be attempted until the woman has, under the direction of a physician skilled in the method, determined for three successive months exactly when ovulation has occurred. For this, she uses basal body temperatures as well as the calendar method of calculating.

The rhythm method is taught in Planned Parenthood Centers and by most doctors.

Fear of Infidelity

Perhaps this fourth fear is widespread because infidelity itself is widespread. No one knows exactly how extensive it is, but studies indicate that at some time during their married lives, many husbands and wives are untrue to their spouses.

There are certain basic facts about infidelity. First, it rarely happens at all if the couple is genuinely happy. And when it does occur in a basically happy marriage, more men than women are apt to be unfaithful. The ratio has been estimated at three or four to one.

Some men, even those with good marriages, cannot resist temptation. Business trips, conventions, attempts to prove to themselves and others that they are "really one of the boys," long absences from home—these are all factors in infidelity. If the marriage is a sound, happy one, the wife may never be aware of the situation, and if the male admits straying occasionally, I suspect that the loving wife most usually forgives and forgets.

If she does not, but chooses to use the incident as a weapon, or as a basis for frequent recrimination, she may destroy the happy foundation of the marriage. I'm reminded of a case history which proves the point.

A young executive admitted to his wife that while on a business trip he had had intercourse with an utter stranger, being intoxicated at the time. Instead of forgiving him, the wife carried on about it for months, and interpreted all of his subsequent actions in the light of this one incident.

"We were happy for five years until this happened," the husband told a doctor friend. "Then everything changed. If I had never told my wife about it, we'd be happy as ever today. I guess I was a fool for wanting to clear my conscience as much as possible."

This couple is not divorced, but the wife refuses to accept her husband's honest attempts to make amends, and I suspect that the marriage is headed for a tragic showdown.

The Sexually Unhappy Marriage

If a couple is sexually unhappy, the possibility of infidelity is far greater. Then, one or the other mate may actually seek an extramarital affair. How to guard against this damaging occurrence?

Studies indicate that four factors play prominent roles with males who stray. The order presented here is not in order of importance. (I doubt if that is known.) First, in the case of the straying male, there is the factor of greater frequency of sexual need. The husband feels he must have intercourse or some kind of sexual activity more often than his wife, and this disparity may remain unresolved for a long time.

Second, the male feels that the sexual play aspect which he so enjoys is somehow unacceptable to his wife; third, the wife may reject one or another form of stimulation, especially oral stimulation; and finally, the husband may feel lack of respect in the home, and that his wife is really the dominant figure in the marriage. His infidelity may represent an attempt to find a woman who will look up to him and reaffirm his maleness.

Insofar as the woman is concerned, there are, I think, some similar factors at the root of infidelity and some dissimilar ones. Lack of sexual satisfaction is certainly basic to the woman who strays. Inability to reach orgasm may be the most important consideration here. She may find her husband coarse and overbearing in his approach to her. Further, I feel that some women stray because they want to be dominated by a man, but find that their husbands simply cannot achieve this domination.

My advice concerning infidelity will be brief. First, forgiveness can be golden, but it should not become a habit. If one or the other mate strays, it is time to re-evaluate the entire marriage soberly and without undue emotion. Husband and wife should sit down together, reassess the marriage and try to discover what is wrong.

A certain amount of compromise will be necessary if the problem stems from unfulfilled sexual needs. Again, it is appropriate to rerun the memory film to discover why husband or wife does or does not accept a technique, an advance, or a belief about marital sex.

Let's look for a moment at the four-in-five marriages in which there is no infidelity. I suspect these marriages have some of the following in common: the couple actively seeks information and advice on all phases of marriage including sex; the couple grows in interests, in devotion to each other and in spiritual feelings of mutual love; and finally, the couple takes little for granted in marriage. Rather, husband and wife know that happiness needs to be worked for, and that happiness is derived mainly from mutual respect, admiration and interest.

Thus, we have seen that in the solution of four typical fears concerning marital sex, there are some common denominators. These are information, initiative, understanding, awareness, ability to compromise, devotion and mature trust in oneself and in the partner.

I shall never forget the experience of a wife in New England. Momentarily, she had forgotten some of these ingredients for a sustained and happy marriage when, for five nights in a row, her husband failed to come home before 10 P.M. She was despondent. What was he doing? She asked, but he gave her only evasive answers. She imagined the worst: another woman, divorce or separation, the end of the marriage.

One night soon after the five late nights, her husband came home beaming. He had negotiated for the purchase of a choice piece of property and the new home was to be a surprise—for the wife who had been so distraught. He had been out late after work with real estate and building people.

Other woman? None existed. The wife had forgotten to trust, to believe and to show the regard for her husband that he obviously was showing for her.

9

Hate and Hostility

This is an age of hate. The air is full of it. And not just across the water, either, but right in our own back yards. It is important to consider hate and hostility because they can be so destructive to every phase of married life, including sex.

Some Saturday morning stand at the meat counter of your supermarket for an hour or so. Listen to the honeyed tones in which women address the butcher. That's so he will give them just the right cut. Then listen to these same women as they talk to their children or to their husbands.

You may be amazed to hear the pent-up and sometimes almost violent hate in the voice and manner of the mother as she says to her child, "How often do I have to tell you not to put your fingers on the glass case." Or to the husband, "I *told* you not to call Jim and invite him over."

In a way, the children and husband are helpless captives. They can reply, of course, but relatively ineffectually. Actually, they are in a position where they must take this expression of hatred. But let the child or husband suddenly fall ill and the relationship is changed. The hostile wife changes her tune. Love and devotion become uppermost in her feelings. Why, then, most of the time does she use the familiarity of the family relationship to express deep hostility toward these comparatively helpless possessions of hers?

The story is told of a temperamental Italian conductor who was extremely disappointed by his first rehearsal with an orchestra.

"What's the matter?" he asked. "You are supposed to be playing '*con amore*.' Instead you are playing like a bunch of married men!"

Was the implication of the conductor's remarks that marriage kills love? Can't a married man or woman act and feel "*con amore*"? As a matter of fact, why can't we act with love in everything we do and say, and toward everyone?

The Anatomy of Hate in Marriage

I am going to discuss eight factors which relate to hate in marriage. I feel that this subject has been largely underplayed because virtually no husband or wife wants to admit that he or she is capable of hate toward the other, married life itself, sex, or the children.

What makes such hate? Prejudice, unfulfilled ambition, unrealized emotional and financial goals, erroneous teaching, attempts to conform to arbitrary standards—all these and more contribute to the sickness of hate in our time. Some people are so full of hate they must express it to anyone they meet. But the majority are sweet as sugar to comparative strangers, and reserve their bitterness for those who are closest and supposedly dearest to them.

Why is the victim of hatred usually close to the person who hates? The victim often has a quality of helplessness about him that attracts hate. Give a bitter person an inch of success in spraying his venom and he wants a mile. Curiously, though, the bitter person, the hater, also is, in a sense, the real victim. For hate is even more destructive to the hater than to the one who is hated.

It should be remembered by husbands and wives that hatred has a boomerang effect. It returns to cause unhappiness, discontent and bitterness. This is true, it seems to me, in every phase of marriage. If sex is the source of long-term marital hatred, solving the sexual problem may help to dissolve the hatred itself.

Hatred of Your Partner

I would like to stress that some hatred and hostility are normal components of marriage. By this I mean hatred in a short-term sense, for few of us can be married for any length of time without feeling genuine hate for our partners at one time or another. There comes a moment, perhaps during or after an argument, when you say to yourself, "Why, this person is perfectly dreadful—an absolute stranger to me. What a terrible thing to be tied to such a person. I had no idea of this when I married."

Then, in the overwhelming majority of cases, there is a brief lapse of time—an hour, two hours, a day—and the perspective returns to normal. Hatred disappears. You begin to see your partner as the beloved person you married, not as the terrible stranger. This type of occurrence is almost inevitable in every marriage and need not be destructive when it happens only infrequently.

However, a marriage is in trouble when bitter feelings become frequent. Sooner or later, a general climate of hostility develops. There's tension in the air, and everyone in the family feels its effects. This is the family that remains together on the weakest kind of thread. It is the family whose members want to leave, to get out, because they find the climate so poisonous and destructive.

As I have said, sex can often be the cause of this type of destructive hatred, but the causes are virtually endless. There is the case of the man who so feared that he would hurt his wife during intercourse that he abstained almost completely. Soon, he began to hate himself for lacking what he considered to be manliness, and he began to hate his wife for the fragility he imagined in her. Luckily, this couple sought competent advice just as they were on the brink of divorce.

Hate arising from sexuality can result from a mannerism of wife or husband, a demand, a little inconsiderate habit. But it is likelier to arise from something much more deep-seated. That is why persons who continue to hate usually require extensive counseling, if not psychiatric care itself.

A twenty-four-year-old wife I know began to hate her husband intensely. She believed that he would never be an adequate provider. Of course, to this young woman, "adequate" had its own definition. She wanted extremely expensive clothes, a big car, lavish vacations. She was not content to keep up with the Joneses, she wanted desperately to outdistance them.

As an expression of her hatred, she decided to punish her husband by having an extramarital affair. She did—with one of the neighbors. Shortly afterward, the couple was divorced, but prior to the divorce it was revealed that the wife took special pains to taunt her husband about her lover. She discussed quite openly his prowess in bed, and praised everything from the size of his genital organs to the size of his bank balance. She said that only her lover had brought her "true happiness."

This woman's behavior obviously is indicative of deep emotional upset, needing psychiatric care. I present this case merely to show what a dangerous feeling hate can become in regard to physical love in marriage.

Then there is the case of the married couple which almost ended in divorce because of hostility born out of misunderstanding. This is extremely common.

A twenty-six-year-old wife began to think that her husband had married her only for physical reasons. Without sex, she thought, her husband would be totally uninterested in their marriage. This feeling intensified until it became a form of hate, and was further intensified by an occasional remark made by her husband concerning the pleasures he gained from sex.

Soon, the wife began to refuse her husband's advances. She made all sorts of excuses, none of which pleased him in the least. Finally, he became furious with her and accused her of turning "cold" toward him. Luckily, they were directed to the doctor of a friend who discussed the entire problem with them.

The wife reluctantly admitted that she thought her husband liked only the sexual aspect of their marriage. The husband, in turn, convinced her that this was entirely untrue. Since the couple received help, they have been happy. That wife forgot a fact of marriage which many wives overlook: if the husband wanted only sex, he would hardly have had to marry in order to get it. Obviously from his standpoint there was a good deal more to the marriage.

At times, some behavior characteristic in or out of the bedroom can lead to a feeling of revulsion akin to hate on the part of one or the other marriage partner. A common one occurred in the marriage of two twenty-year-olds. As newlyweds, they were comparatively unskilled in the art of love.

The husband, overzealous, typically would grasp his wife roughly in bed and fairly smother her with affection. With but little precoital play, he would be prepared for the final act. This lack of finesse repelled his wife, who began to think of her new husband as coarse and vulgar.

Fortunately, these two were mature even for their years. She told him about her feelings one evening and he resolved to be more gentle in his amorous approach to her. This was the beginning of their real married life.

Hate As a Weapon

Many of us fool ourselves into believing that we are accomplishing something positive when we utilize hate as a weapon. I know a husband who obtained positive proof that his wife had had intercourse once with another man. In his own destructive way, he has used this information ever since.

He keeps reminding his wife of the incident. He uses his knowledge like a whip, and the whip has a barb in it. Whenever something in the home displeases him, no matter how trivial, he brings out the whip and flicks it in her face. He rationalizes that he is holding the proof of her misstep ever before her so that she will never misbehave again, but the wife, the children and the husband himself have suffered deeply because the entire family relationship has been permeated by this climate of hatred and tortured feelings.

I have mentioned how husbands and wives sometimes use sex as a bargaining weapon or as reward and punishment. It should never be used in such ways. Sex is not a football to be kicked whenever you want to make a goal. In particular, it should never be used to prove that one of the mates is superior to or stronger than the other. Nor should sex be used as retaliation against your spouse's hate, or as a protection from it.

With only one lifetime in which to enjoy marriage and family, why waste a moment of it in hating? This is one emotion that will surely poison the lives of all within reach of it.

Envy

Very often, the antidote for envy lies in admitting it to yourself and to your partner. This feeling in particular can be softened once it is placed out in the open, in the clear light of day. Next, the jealous individual should analyze the source of his jealousy. Does the person whom you envy really have the qualities you attribute to him? Perhaps. More probably not, or else those qualities soon are discovered to be quite commonplace.

Does it help to emulate the person for whom you feel jealousy? I think not. Be yourself. Your spouse found the qualities within you most attractive at the time you were married. Now the task is to grow with your partner, socially, intellectually and emotionally.

Hostility Based on Career

At times, hostility in marriage results from the fact that both husband and wife have separate careers and the wife seems the more successful of the two.

In one case I know of, this caused real emotional pain for a while. A thirty-three-year-old career woman simply refused to quit her job and raise a family. She told her husband that her income was too important to them. Furthermore, she said, her career would lead to a brilliant future and series of promotions.

This attitude caused a real breach in the marriage. The husband began to feel inferior. He saw his initiative as man of the house being threatened. Also, he had a genuine desire for children. A vital part of this case cannot, of course, be overlooked. This man and his wife were deeply in love. There was no thought here of divorce or of separation.

They sat down one night and totaled their earnings which together added up to a considerable sum. Could they get along well on less? they asked each other. Over a period of time, a compromise was reached.

The wife discovered that her services were so much in demand that she could work for as little as two days a week for part pay. That income, however, plus her husband's, would be adequate, they decided. Today, they have a lovely baby girl. The wife is still in touch with her career world and she has her child as well. In a sense, that couple found that, by compromise, they could have their cake and eat it too.

Productive Hostility

There is, however, one good side to hostility, for the hostile individual has a choice: he can keep right on being hostile, or he can do something positive about it.

On a very simple level, productive hostility can be explained this way: If you step off the curb and see a ten-ton truck bearing down on you, the normal reaction is to jump back on the curb. You're angry about the incident perhaps, but you did not allow your anger to render you immobile. If you had, you would have been killed. In a sense, the same idea pertains to hostility in marriage.

Let's say you find yourself hostile toward your partner. Your hostility may be caused by one of a hundred things, his habits, attitudes, desires, values in life. If you keep this hostility pent up in you, it will only explode at a later date. If you reveal your hostility, then you and your spouse, as mature, level-headed individuals, can together set about lessening the cause of the hostility.

Very often, a husband will not even be aware of the fact that what he thinks or does serves to alienate his wife; and the reverse is true, too. Exposure of the facts in the situation is one of the healthiest of all approaches. Such exposure often serves to show how productive hostility can be.

Conflict Solving

Marriages usually do not start off solid as the Rock of Gibraltar. Most of them are somewhat shaky at the beginning. There is an air of exploration and unsteadiness about the early marriage which is perfectly understandable. Two people, with different conditioning, habits and ideas, suddenly are man and wife. It is inevitable that conflict should arise. The point is this: with each conflict that is resolved in marriage, the marriage itself is likely to be strengthened. Think of how secure and triumphant the couple feels after solving together a problem associated with some phase of marital sex. A whole new world opens up for them. This does not mean that there will be no further conflict. Almost certainly there will be. But when it comes, the couple will be just that much better prepared to handle it.

I suppose that some readers are wondering what on earth I am talking about. They cannot conceive of themselves as hating, as using hate as a weapon, as being jealous or in conflict. Yes, of course they got cross with their husbands or wives last night. And they certainly had to speak sharply to the children this morning. But, after all, they are human, aren't they? Being cross and speaking sharply—that's human, isn't it?

This, of course, is where self-analysis and honesty with self must come into the picture. It is extremely difficult to know, at a given moment, how you really feel about something important to you. It is extremely difficult to distinguish between momentary annoyance, which is quite human, and the use of such a moment to express a far deeper, more destructive feeling, which is vented on a person who may have had very little to do with it —usually a husband, wife or child.

This book is not supposed to be a substitute for psychiatric treatment, nor to express the psychoanalytic viewpoint. The person who really is subject to deep hatred and who expresses it will perhaps be the last one to realize it from reading these pages, for it may well be too difficult a thing to face and to admit to oneself.

However, we can all benefit from taking inventory of ourselves now and again. I think we will find, a good deal of the time, that we simply are suffering from our own bad habits. It is easy to get into the bad habit of speaking roughly and sharply to someone you love. This is taking unfair advantage of a close relationship—one so close that the other person really is helpless in it. If we look deeply into ourselves, and try hard to understand just what our real motives are, most of us will find that it is just as easy to allow love to speak as it is hate.

We have only one lifetime in which to live a marriage. What a shame to allow hate to dominate any of marriage's precious moments. What a shame to risk spoiling a single memory or a relationship with the seeds of destruction.

Much as we later wish we could, it is impossible to relive those unhappy moments when hate got the better of us.

10

Infertility—Couples Without Children

About 5,000,000 American couples, one in ten, who want children have none. If they have tried for two years or longer to achieve normal pregnancy and failed, they are then considered by doctors to be "infertile."

Infertility is one of the most complex, mysterious and at times happily surprising problems in medicine. While four out of ten infertile couples can be helped, medically, to have their own children, therapy may be long and arduous. Tensions of the couple may play a vital role. Some couples who have nothing organically wrong may actually be victims of their emotions, a factor increasingly implicated as a possible cause of infertility. Of course, the primary causes are physiological.

False Ideas About Infertility

One of the most common misconceptions concerning infertility involves medical contraception. It is sometimes believed that if a couple has used contraceptives they render themselves infertile. This is simply not so. If there were any truth at all to this myth, medical contraception would not be taught in the obstetrical courses of virtually every non-Catholic medical school on the American continent. Instead, here is what happens: a couple may not *discover* their infertility until *after* they have stopped using medical contraceptives; then they proceed to lay the blame on the contraceptives, when, in fact, they were infertile from the outset.

This is why young couples are advised to postpone the first pregnancy for no more than two years. Thus, if there is an infertility problem, it will be discovered early. Sometimes diagnosis and treatment of infertility takes a year or two. Inasmuch as youth favors fertility, the sooner treatment is initiated the better the chances for conception and normal pregnancy.

There are two other common beliefs about infertility which you may have heard. One would have us believe that frequency of intercourse is related to the male's "sperm strength." In other words, the more frequent the instances of intercourse, the "weaker" the sperm. This is not so. Actually, according to many excellent studies, some experts hold that exactly the opposite is true. The second belief is that organ disproportion or misplacement is a common cause of infertility. Thus, some couples are convinced that the male's penis is inadequate, or the woman's uterus "tipped," and that these factors cause infertility. Inadequacy from the organic standpoint is rarely a cause.

Tensions of the Infertile Couple

Actually, the couple that goes along for three, five, seven years without children may suffer two distinct types of tension. One relates to the failure to conceive; the other may be more deep-rooted, involving early childhood conditioning, career or the marriage itself. Let's discuss the first type first.

Typically, the infertile couple may acquire a real sense of inferiority because they are childless. They may become guilt-ridden, accuse themselves or their mates, openly or secretly, and have profound feelings of self-recrimination, particularly if they have not sought professional help in locating the real cause of their difficulty.

Such tensions are even doubly tragic when you stop to consider that they might themselves give rise to further tensions which can prevent conception. Thus, tension builds on tension to produce a circular process of unhappiness. The best antidote is to consult a gynecologist who specializes in treating cases of infertility, the gynecological department of the medical school nearest you, or one of the twenty-five long-established and successful infertility clinics sponsored, nation-wide, by the Planned Parenthood Federation of America.

The Planned Parenthood Federation assumed leadership in establishing infertility services as long as twenty-five years ago, and in the past fifteen years, great progress has been made in the field of infertility. It has now become a subspecialty of obstetrics and gynecology. Sixteen years ago, the American Society for the Study of Sterility was established. It has spurred research in this field, and hopeful results are being reported at a truly heartening rate. In addition, many more clinics have been set up by medical schools and hospitals for study and treatment of the infertile couple.

Tensions That Cause Infertility

One of the findings of medical research is that tensions themselves, somehow, appear to prevent conception or normal pregnancy. This finding only serves to illustrate the great force exerted on all phases of our lives by our emotions. Tensions that prevent conception are varied indeed. The wife or husband or both may subconsciously fear the prospect of becoming parents, or the wife may fear childbirth itself, or they may consider the addition of a child an unbearable burden.

In addition, deep-seated tensions coming from the wife's childhood itself may cause infertility. Frequently, these are mysterious even to the doctor, and may or may not be cleared up spontaneously. The tensions may exist, become reduced in intensity through therapy, and conception may follow. One of the truly amazing facts of infertility treatment is that some tension-ridden women conceive without formal psychotherapy; others conceive after a single visit to a specialist or infertility clinic; still others conceive after they receive only reassurances and emotional "booster shots" from their doctors.

One doctor I know tells the following story: A thirty-five-year-old woman who was childless had convinced herself that she would never have a baby. She was high-strung emotionally and it is possible that her emotions played a major role in her infertility. The doctor and patient talked for a long time. He was reassuring and his manner radiated confidence.

"I'm going to have a baby," the patient said after several visits. "I know it. There's something about your approach to this whole problem that gives me a great feeling. I've never felt so assured in all my life!"

Sure enough, she conceived shortly afterward and carried the full nine months. That doctor's conclusion, based on years of experience with such patients: "Emotional factors were extremely important in this case. If the woman gains total confidence in her doctor, that's half the battle. In this particular case, there was no real treatment, except for those little chats which were designed to help the patient gain confidence in herself."

The cases of emotional involvement in infertility go on and on. There's the case of the couple infertile for five years. Grudgingly, they admitted that they had never previously wanted a baby, so they had had intercourse only once or twice a month. This in itself required psychotherapy. There's the couple who were childless and both somewhat disturbed. Both sought psychotherapy and they now have a child.

There's even the case of a woman who went to an infertility clinic for four and a half years, meticulously showing up for every appointment. At the end of that time, she made a shamefaced admission. Her husband wanted children, but she was afraid of childbirth. As a result, she came to the clinic, but for the entire four and a half years she admitted, "I used contraceptives each time we had intercourse." Imagine the reaction of the doctors! This woman was "infertile" because she simply did not want to be anything else. Psychiatric treatment was suggested for her.

Perhaps the most amazing aspect of infertility therapy is that some women require only the comfort and reassurance that doctors are available to treat them if anything goes wrong. Such women require no therapy whatsoever. Recently, at a medical meeting, a renowned specialist from Australia reported that of one hundred infertile women, twenty had conceived without any form of therapy. A single visit to the clinic was therapy enough!

The implication is obvious. Infertility cannot be treated unless husband and wife have a mature attitude about their problem, decide to seek therapy and then follow doctor's orders.

Tensions of the infertile couple can be dissolved or greatly lessened by following such a course.

I know of one couple who had been married ten years before they had their first child. For seven of those years, they had gone from doctor to doctor seeking the cause of the infertility. They had confidence in none of the doctors, thus did not stay for a prolonged period under the care of any of them. Finally, they made up their minds that they would remain with one doctor for at least a year and were rewarded by a successful pregnancy in due time.

The moral of this story: Find a physician or infertility clinic in whom you have complete trust, continue visits until you are told to stop. Remember, it may take several years for success.

Examination for Infertility

Another of the great myths surrounding infertility is that it is almost always "the wife's fault" or "the husband's fault." This belief, of course, can create great anxiety in one or the other. The truth is that infertility, like marriage itself, is a fifty-fifty affair. In about half the cases, the wife is the one who needs therapy, in the other half, the husband, sometimes it is both.

Thus, infertility specialists recognize that it is essential to study both husband and wife with equal attention and care. In fact, the American Society for the Study of Sterility indicates that the first step is to consider husband and wife as a biologic unit—which indeed they are. Here is how the famed Margaret Sanger Bureau in New York City, the largest infertility service in the U. S. and a pioneer in infertility therapy, studies the infertile couple.

First, complete medical histories are taken of husband and wife. The marital history of the couple is then studied—the length thus far of marriage, sexual patterns of the marriage, what they have already done to achieve pregnancy. The husband is given a complete physical examination as is the wife, in order to seek and define possible physical causes of the infertility.

Next, the husband is studied sexually. His organs are examined. Tests are performed on his seminal fluid to determine its quality, to assure that there is an adequate number of normal sperm cells. As I have said, nature has provided an enormous number, normally two hundred million sperm at each orgasm. Experts consider a male to be an infertility problem when the number of sperm at each ejaculation is significantly lower. Below eighteen million per ejaculation, pregnancy rarely is achieved.

Not only is the sperm number studied, but the quality of the sperm is analyzed. The sizes and shapes of the sperm cells are examined microscopically to determine if the cells are normal and uniform in appearance and to see if their movement is rapid, vigorous and prolonged.

Study of the Woman

The wife's genital tract is examined thoroughly. Primarily, the doctor seeks abnormalities or disease. Most important is the degree of openness of the Fallopian tubes, which can be determined by a relatively simple test. In addition, it is usual to take a small amount of tissue from the lining of the uterus to determine if the woman is secreting normal hormones. Finally, various studies can be made to ascertain the functioning of the endocrine glands.

Surveying Tension

During all this time, the examining doctor has been able to form some sort of impression as to the emotional status of the couple. This is important because studies of other organs of the body have shown conclusively that tension can alter these various organs and their performance. For instance, studies show that fear, anxiety and anger so affect the lining of the stomach as to diminish its ability to manufacture digestive juices, with resultant disturbance of the entire digestive process. Studies have also shown that such tensions can affect the mechanisms of speech, hearing, heart rate, bowel function and other physical functions. We know that anxiety can give us rashes, headaches, nausea, dizziness and a whole set of irritating ailments. It can even cause sudden blindness. Most of these fall into the category of psychosomatic disorders.

Such observations have led doctors to believe that tensions can have a damaging effect on ovulation or on the Fallopian tubes and thus on the entire mechanism of conception. We also know that tensions can have profound effects on the male's desire for intercourse and his performance during intercourse.

It is a mistake, however, to believe that infertility is primarily a psychic problem. True, the infertile couple as a rule develops, or has had, emotional problems, for infertility itself does pack a tremendous emotional wallop. But with most infertile patients, the physical problem overshadows the psychic one as the true cause of the infertility.

A young couple I know were told by one doctor that they were both perfectly healthy. He said, "Your problem *must* be emotional."

"Are you sure that you are happy?" he asked. "Go home and ask yourselves some searching questions about your marriage. I think that there must be much in it that remains unresolved. When you solve your emotional problems, come back and see me."

This on the basis of a single superficial examination of the husband and wife! Actually, that couple was extremely happy and had comparatively few emotional problems. But they did inventory their marriage and decided it was a sound one.

Someone then recommended the Margaret Sanger Bureau,

where a simple physical problem was eventually discovered in the wife. It was treated at the Bureau, cleared up, and the wife immediately became pregnant. This case illustrates the importance of thorough study by experts before final diagnosis can be made.

Therapy for Physical Impairment

There are a variety of treatments possible for the infertile couple, depending on the nature of the physical problem.

Tubal Insufflation

This is a technique used in both diagnosis and therapy of blocked Fallopian tubes. It was devised by the late Dr. Isidor Rubin and thus is known as the Rubin test. This technique seeks to open the tubes with gentle air pressure. In a good many cases it has proven successful. Some doctors report that in as many as 25 percent of selected cases the Rubin test can prove of real benefit.

Tubal Surgery

In a few special cases, the doctor may attempt to repair blocked Fallopian tubes by means of surgery. This has sometimes been successful, even among a few cases which had been considered utterly hopeless, perhaps 10 to 30 percent of selected cases. I recall the case of a twenty-seven-year-old New York wife who was on the operating table when one of the assisting physicians remarked, "Why attempt surgery on this patient? Isn't there too slight a chance of success?"

"While any kind of a chance exists," the surgeon said, "we ought to take it. At least that's the way the patient feels about it."

The operation was a success, and that woman now has a two-year-old boy. After her delivery, the father, who also had undergone therapy for infertility and who had many of the anxieties both of the infertile person and of the new father, came up to the obstetrician and asked excitedly, "Doctor, do you think there's a chance that she'll be able to have another child?" Without having seen his firstborn, he was already concerned with a possible second.

Use of X-ray or Hormones

Certain women ovulate infrequently or with extreme irregularity. For these, X-ray has been tried and occasionally there is success in establishing regular cycles. Because of present-day awareness of the dangers of overradiation, such therapy must be carried out only by a physician known to specialize in this method. One such outstanding authority says that with anovulatory women (those who ovulate infrequently) up to 30 percent success can be achieved by means of X-ray. In addition, some hormones or new hormone-like substances are now found to be sometimes helpful in stimulating ovulation in the woman and sperm-formation in the man.

Your Temperature—Blessing and Curse

The commonest cause of sexual tensions among the infertile revolves around taking the wife's temperature, which must be done to determine the wife's fertile period. Indeed, when it was discovered more than a generation ago that the basal temperature could serve to indicate the period of ovulation, the finding was hailed throughout the world. There are, as a result, a good many "temperature babies," but the entire business of temperature taking should be viewed as a mixed blessing.

If you count the menstrual cycle as beginning on the first day of menstruation, it is generally considered that ovulation (release of the ovum to be fertilized) takes place about 14 days before the onset of the next menstrual period. The difficulty lies in predicting which day will be the first day of the next period. If the menstrual period of a woman starts on March 1, let's say, and ordinarily she had a 30-day period, ovulation most probably would occur around March 16. Or, if she had a 28-day period, it would take place around March 14. But no woman is ever exactly regular, and one or two days' variation can make all the difference in successful infertility therapy.

Now, the day of ovulation itself can be established most accurately by taking the basal temperature, that is, the body temperature on awakening before the woman sets foot out of bed. When the record of these basal temperatures is set down on a simple sheet of graph paper, it can usually be observed that there is a sudden rise of a few tenths of a degree just before ovulation followed by a sharp, rapid drop just afterward. If fertilization should occur, there will be no drop, and the original temperature rise before ovulation will be maintained.

These changes in temperature are so slight that a special thermometer has been devised that shows temperatures only between 98 and 100 degrees. Thus, it becomes very simple to spot a rise of as little as a tenth of a degree on this magnified scale.

Many couples who have tried to achieve pregnancy without success hear about the basal temperature method and try it on their own. This is wrong for many reasons, because first of all, they should have a complete infertility examination to make sure that there is nothing physically wrong. But perhaps the most important reason is that without the guidance of a skilled physician the thermometer tends to become a useless dictator. It dictates the time at which the couple must have intercourse. As a result, tension is liable to arise because even with a cooperative husband, after a while it is difficult for the sexual relationship to be ordered up à la carte at the bidding of a gadget, and many couples who have tried this have been discouraged to discover that all the time, because of their lack of knowledge of how to interpret the temperature curve, they were actually having intercourse at the wrong intervals.

Wives become tense at the period when the temperature may be expected to fluctuate and husbands rebel at the announcement, "Today, now!" They come to feel as if their only function is to perform a physical act that loses its meaning in the presence of the temperature chart and thermometer. Actually, many husbands have threatened to throw the thermometer out the window—and some have done so!

Adoption

No doubt you have heard of the following situation: A couple is childless for years. Infertility examinations and treatment have yielded no result. Finally, after much discussion, they decide to adopt a child, a procedure that takes time. At long last, the legal technicalities are worked out and the child is theirs. Shortly thereafter, this "infertile" couple conceives. Lo and behold, this same husband and wife now have their own child! Medical authorities point out that this not only happens, but that it is fairly common. Why?

No one knows exactly, but some doctors believe that when the adopted child comes into the home, somehow tensions are reduced for husband, wife or both. In this state of reduced tensions, the mother who is no longer worrying about having children—her adopted one is there—somehow becomes able to conceive.

When to Adopt

As I have said, infertility is fraught with tension. It is difficult, if not impossible, to be tension-free when tests and probings are being made into your sex life. Furthermore, as I indicated couples have demonstrated, it is exceedingly difficult to have to regulate your sexual life, month after month, by the calendar or by the thermometer.

If all therapeutic measures for the infertile couple have been tried and pregnancy is not achieved in two to four years, most doctors agree that the couple would do well to consider adoption. The younger the couple, the better the chance of obtaining a child for adoption, even if they must wait a year or two. If it is carried out properly, adoption can be tremendously successful. With present-day safeguards, it is highly unlikely that the child will be subnormal or defective.

In fact, many adoption agencies feel that the safeguards have been made a little too stringent. As a result, many a fine couple who would have made wonderful parents have been denied this great privilege because the agency has found them just a bit "too old." There are additional rigid requirements surrounding adoption. Because interfaith adoptions are almost universally prohibited either by rulings or practice, the children of some faiths remain in orphanages year after year because adoptive parents of the same faiths are not as numerous as those of other faiths. Tragically, too, there are racial barriers to adoption, but some agencies and parents are beginning to realize that a lovable human being is lovable no matter if he be Negro, Chinese, Japanese or Korean. As a result, Negro and Oriental children are being increasingly adopted by white families—but not rapidly enough to lower the level of such lonely little beings in their crowded orphanages.

The Black Market in Babies

The adoption racket flourishes, however. A frightened, distraught, unwed white mother still is coerced into giving up her child, or gives him up willingly to a mercenary attorney, nurse or physician. What happens? The baby is actually "sold" to an anxious couple willing to pay up to several thousand dollars "for legal and medical expenses." A United States subcommittee investigating this tragic "selling of flesh" revealed that some couples have paid up to $10,000 per baby to the unscrupulous baby brokers.

The dangers of obtaining a baby through the black market should be obvious. There is no "back-check" to determine who the parents of the adoptive child are, and no dependable attempt is made to determine if the child is defective. Finally, no one has protected the child by determining whether the adoptive parents are, indeed, worthy of having one. Adoption by financial capability alone is certainly no criterion. The U. S. Children's Bureau states that this evil racket can be fought effectively only if couples insist on adopting through well-recognized agencies and if mothers who decide that they must give up their babies refuse to relinquish them except to such agencies.

Successful Adoption

In one of the finest families I know, the wife was told by her physician that her chances of conceiving were probably nil. She proceeded to adopt three children at intervals of two years. Then, lo and behold, she became pregnant twice. In that family, it would be exceedingly difficult for an outsider to determine which were the three adopted children and which were their two "own"—or which were grandchildren by the adopted children and which by their "own."

Patience Is Essential

To sum up, I must stress that couples should not worry about infertility if they have tried for a baby only three, six or ten months. Pregnancy may not come for a year, eighteen months or even longer. If, however, after trying for well over a year, you have not succeeded, you should go to an infertility specialist or an infertility clinic, if only to find out when thorough studies should be started.

During the period of diagnosis and therapy, about four out of every ten couples will achieve pregnancy at one time or another. Generally, after two years or so of follow-up without conception, a diagnosis of true infertility may be made. Then it would be wise, during the usual lengthy adoption wait, for the couple to resume normal married life without any organized effort to achieve pregnancy, and to be as relaxed as possible and enjoy life together to its fullest.

Harking back to something I mentioned before—that adoption itself can be therapeutic for the infertile couple—I must cite the case of the college professor and his wife who after many years decided to adopt.

One agency offered this couple a fine set of twin infant boys. With hearts overflowing, the professor and his wife agreed to adopt them. Very shortly afterward, another adoption agency offered them beautiful twin baby girls. The couple were so happy with their first two that after some prayerful consideration of their means, they accepted the two little girls joyfully. Total: four children.

Shortly thereafter, the wife found herself pregnant, and eventually delivered—twins! A girl and a boy. Total: three boys and three girls, all under two years of age, and being taken care of on a professor's salary. The last I heard: all doing wonderfully!

11

Sexual Tensions After the First Baby

Ask the average engaged couple if they want children and they will answer without any hesitation whatever, "Of course we do. No marriage is complete without children."

Actually, however, the sober facts about having children are usually as unreal to them as are the facts about marriage itself. Intellectually, this couple may have faced the problems of parenthood, with its constant and, at times, incredible demands. The likelihood, though, is that they have not faced the facts emotionally. They have little idea that it is one thing to lose sleep because of a late party and quite another to lose it with a crying or demanding baby. The two causes may result in exactly the same amount of sleep loss, but somehow they evoke different feelings about that loss.

In a sense, reactions to parenthood take place on two levels, the spiritual and the mechanical. Spiritually, a baby can strengthen the emotional ties of a household. Mechanically, caring for a baby can cause considerable dislocation in the home.

Mechanical First-Babyitis

Even in this day of diaper services and automatic washing machines, there are still unpleasantly (to most people) soiled diapers to be coped with, and in addition the accompanying soiled little bottom for which there is no automatic washer or service. Then, there are the inevitable sour milk odors when the baby burps—sometimes on your best clothes. In addition, there is the added necessity of getting the baby out into the fresh air regularly, without you and the baby freezing or roasting and without interfering with the everlasting round of household duties.

Finally, there comes a moment when the baby ceases to be just a physical little being and begins to be an emotional one with quite clear-cut demands on your inner self, demands that require patience, understanding and denial of what *you* want to do. You might want to spend the afternoon watching television or reading or doing your nails or sleeping, but you cannot because the baby has a cold, wants attention or whines until you are frantic.

Although the answer to the question, "Do you want babies?" almost always comes immediately, "Yes," the answer to the question, "*Why* do you want babies," probably would be delayed. Few people have ever thought about the answer to that one. It is not an answer which has to do with thinking or the intellect, but rather with the deepest kinds of feelings. These are feelings of love which need to gain expression through the infant, feelings of "oneness" with youngsters, feelings of having achieved the ultimate in creative endeavor in life, feelings of wanting this concrete evidence that you and your mate are truly "one flesh." There are many other feelings, of course, that are far less clearly defined.

Rebound Tensions

The very fact that the feelings connected with having a baby are so deep, and at the same time so unknown, is one explanation of why the rebound emotions after the first child are frequently as strong as they are. A young man and woman have barely plunged into that first great experience of living together, when, in a year or so, they are plunged into an amazing extension of that experience. Suddenly, they must live as three people instead of two, under conditions that I indicated earlier can be extremely demanding. Inevitably, there will be disagreements, harsh words, arguments.

In this connection, we must mention an important fact. If their initial relationship has not had the time or the opportunity to develop into a really strong one, the new demands of parenthood can cause considerable stresses and strains. At this point, troubles can really begin. As a matter of fact, in the basically unsound marriage, parenthood can be the precipitating factor which leads to divorce. Thus, it is a fact that there are more divorces among "one-baby families" than among any other category. This is a strong reason why conception of a baby should be planned when the couple feels ready for it. Babies should be born by choice, not by chance.

Changes in the Woman

After the first child, the simple fact alone of the great changes in the woman's body are enough to cause stress in the marriage. Here I would like to mention some of the inevitable factors that can and do cause sexual tensions between husband and wife in this vital period.

First, as I have said, the woman's body has undergone profound changes. For nine months she has nurtured inside herself a new, young life. Processes have been taking place that she is not likely to understand fully. Her womb (uterus) has grown enormously along with the developing baby. Even after the birth, it takes this organ at least six weeks to return to near-normal size.

Of course, the passage of the baby through the birth canal has altered the vagina too, stretching it so that it is no longer the snug passage that it was. It, too, will return to normal size. But the word "normal" here is used with relation to its post-birth, rather than its prebirth size and shape.

Further, the entrance into the vagina may also have changed. Partly, this may be due to the stretching it has undergone and partly to the small nick or episiotomy that is usually performed to permit the baby's head to come through easily in birth, and that is repaired afterward with a few simple stitches. There is some change, too, in the look and feel of the vulva, because of the shaving of the hair in preparation for the birth. This, in itself, creates a very strange feeling in the woman, for it has been a long time since she was without hair in this area of her body. She may feel naked and ashamed before her husband during the weeks that it is growing back.

Her abdomen, too, is not as it once was. It will take some time for her muscles to regain their elasticity. Until then, she may have a soft, flabby feeling in the abdomen, or she may have unattractive folds of wrinkled skin. This, too, may tend to make her feel ugly and ashamed. The discharge that is normal after birth, called "lochia," may also linger for several weeks. It is not copious as a rule, but it is characterized by its own odor which may be disturbing to the young mother.

If she is nursing her baby (most mothers realize now that this is best), she will experience gushes of milk from the breast just before each nursing, when the breasts are full. These gushes may stain her clothing. Certainly, they will provide another kind of body odor to which the mother must become accustomed, and the full sensitive breasts may cause moments of disturbing discomfort when intercourse is resumed, as well as interfere with pleasurable oral stimulation during the nursing period.

The Wife's Question About Sex

Almost inevitably, the new young mother wonders if and how she will be able to function sexually with all of the changes I have mentioned. She asks herself: Will I still be the same kind of wife I was before? Better perhaps? Worse? Will the changes in my body make my husband enjoy me less? Will I ever regain the feeling of youth, freshness and vitality that I had before I became pregnant?

She may be relieved rather than chagrined when the doctor forbids intercourse until the sixth week or so after the baby's birth, for ordinarily, the doctor does not give the go-ahead until after the postpartum examination. She has a sneaking conviction that she has been given a six-week holiday from "that," so she is relieved not to have to worry about anything until then—whether she will respond, whether she will become pregnant again. There are none of these particular anxieties for the short six weeks. But there is still the haunting anxiety of how she will "do" when the six weeks are up.

Postpartum Depression

Perhaps because of the physical changes in the woman, perhaps because of hormonal changes which are not yet understood, a great many new mothers experience postpartum depression. This occurs so often that it cannot be considered abnormal.

Usually, the new mother begins to feel blue without being able to explain why. Such depression comes as a rule shortly after birth and lasts no longer than a few hours, or a day or two. If it persists longer than four or five days, the woman should tell her obstetrician of her problem.

I recall one case which is typical. A twenty-seven-year-old wife had just had her first baby, a boy. Her husband was elated and came home for lunch one day just a week after his wife and baby had returned from the hospital. He found his wife sitting on the bed in tears.

"I'm ugly," she sobbed. "Look at me. I'll never be the same."

"You look wonderful to me, dear," said the startled husband.

"Oh, no, I don't," she said. "I'm all changed. Look at my stomach. Look at me."

The husband sensed what was happening. His wife had a galloping case of postpartum blues. He spent the next hour comforting her, reassuring her that she was more lovely than ever. He had to return to his office shortly afterward, and when he came home for dinner that night, he found his wife no longer in tears.

"I got a book to read about postpartum depression," she said. "That's what I guess I have. But it goes away after a while. I feel much better now."

All that wife needed was a little reassurance that what she experienced was normal. The next morning she felt even better and her depression became just a memory. Of course, not all cases are as simple as that. The depression may come four, six, ten weeks or even longer after the birth. It can compound all other tensions after the first baby.

The Husband's Feelings

From the new father's point of view, there are anxieties too, most of them falling within the normal range. He sees his wife absorbed in the new life which they have created. Does this mean permanent transfer of affection from him?

He may have only a vague idea of what has happened to his wife physically, and he, too, is likely to be full of anxieties about changes which he believes may have taken place in her. He has heard stories that stretching of the birth canal may make his wife "too large." This, he believes, may make it more difficult for him to enjoy intercourse.

The husband knows at this point that his wife has not regained her strength. In addition, she has bottles, diapers, housework and the baby itself to contend with. He wants to be helpful, but secretly, he would like to return to the prebirth status as soon as possible. Meanwhile, he is increasingly anxious about whether intercourse will be as good and fulfilling as it was before.

He visualizes the six-week period as being far from a holiday. Added as it is to the six or so weeks of abstinence previous to the birth, he begins to feel somewhat victimized by circumstance. He wants his wife, but he may be afraid that she has changed so he cannot have her again on his own terms.

I recall the case of a husband who simply would not abide by the doctor's orders to abstain for six weeks prior to birth and six weeks after. He insisted on having intercourse during both periods. His wife was so terrified that some permanent injury would result that she could not respond to her husband in her usual fashion, and intercourse during this time was a complete failure. This left the husband brooding and sullen. How can such occurrences be avoided?

Release from First-Child Tension

Sometimes in the pre- and post-birth "no intercourse" period, a loving wife can offer manual stimulation to her husband. I know of several couples for whom this has effectively decreased "first baby" tensions. Sometimes when the husband is more passive, he will find it easy to do without sexual stimulation during the entire period. Sometimes after the period is over, the husband will want sex frequently, more frequently than before. I suggest that the wife comply with such desires, for the couple together will gradually be working out a new level of adjustment.

All this focuses clearly on a need for considerable readjustment on the part of the married couple with their first child. Increasing the friction in this period is the fact that a readjustment is necessary often before the first real adjustment to marriage itself has been made. This is the point in marriage—after the first child comes—where communication between husband and wife is so important.

Putting your anxieties and your fears into words usually helps to clear them away. Once they are examined closely by the two persons most concerned, they seem to lose their immediacy and force. Also, it is discovered that many of the anxieties have no real foundation. If the husband and wife talk to each other honestly, each will understand the other's problems and each will be spurred to a special effort to help the other.

Baby As a Protection

Supposing, though, that the husband and wife have not learned to talk to each other about sex. Often what happens then is that the baby becomes a sort of protective mechanism, useful to the wife and annoying to the husband. Needless to say, use of the baby in this manner compounds marital tensions.

Typically, the wife says, "I can't now. I was up all night with the baby." "I don't feel like it now because I don't have time. I have to nurse the baby in a few minutes." "I don't want to turn on a light, it might disturb the baby." "My breasts are too full of milk—they'll hurt." "The baby might overhear us." This type of response goes on and on, to the vast irritation of the husband, who reacts to what he hears and takes it literally. In no time at all he begins to wonder if the idea of having a baby was such a good one. He may begin to believe that he has lost more than he has gained by it.

In this situation, it will benefit husbands and wives to realize something that is basic to marriage and to many other life situations. Generally, you do exactly what you want to do. You help yourself do it by finding reasons to support it. This is called "rationalization." All of us rationalize a good deal of the time.

In the particular situation I am discussing now, the wife may well be rationalizing. If she *really* wanted to be near her husband or to have intercourse with him, none of the seemingly good reasons she mentioned would amount to anything at all. Nothing would keep her from him. Why, then, does she *not* want the resumption of the love relationship with her husband? Or, at least, why does she not admit to herself that she is trying to avoid it?

Need for Husbandly Restraint

This is a point in marriage where the man must really check himself a bit. First, he must realize exactly what his wife has gone through in the process of pregnancy and childbirth. If the same thing had happened to his body, with the same marked changes, he, too, might feel that he had undergone a very special experience and deserved to be treated in a very special way.

He might also be rather nervous about the possibility of another pregnancy occurring soon again, before he was ready for it. This does not mean that the husband must baby his wife and give in to her every whim. It does mean that having understood the profound changes and strains that took place in his wife's body, he must also consider the emotional stresses she may be undergoing now because of the readjustments she must make. At this point, he must be prepared to take a long step in growing up. He must become truly the head of the house.

Many men assume that to be head of the house simply means that you are the boss, that what you want and say are law. Alas, it is not as simple as that. Being head of the house is in many ways similar to being the responsible ruler of a country, or the owner of a big business. It can be a very lonely job because you are top man on the totem pole. There is nobody above you and that is not as wonderful as it may sound. It means that you must take the responsibility for the welfare of everyone else below you on the totem pole.

Nobody else shares this responsibility; nobody can advise you. You are "it." And when you are "it" in a family of two that has just become three, you must put your own welfare last. You must do this to assure that the wife whom you love can complete her experience of creating a new life and still emerge thinking and feeling great.

Spoil Your Wife?

Should you spoil her just a little? In a sense, yes, but not in the cheap sense of buying her favors or of giving in to her all the time. What I am referring to is spoiling in the far broader sense of the term. The husband should be big enough to provide emotional support for his wife, sympathize with her and encourage her. He should provide love and guidance and expect the best from his wife without crucifying her when she is not able to live up to the "best." He should put being father and brother and friend to his wife ahead of being lover. If he does this he can be quite sure that she will all the sooner be eager to seek him as lover.

Strengthening Marital Emotions

Some marriages fail to weather the first year or two of babies. I might cite the famous young Hollywood marriage that broke up after three years and two babies. A Hollywood columnist wrote a long item the essence of which was, "Were they really and truly in love when they married?"

Right here and now I would like to say that the emotions most young people feel when they marry are inadequate to carry them for more than two or three years in marriage. They will be terribly unhappy after that unless they have the capacity to grow and deepen so that their emotions also mature.

This may seem rather brutal, but couples who have weathered ten, fifteen, twenty years of marriage and weathered them well will know what I mean. I would like to remind you of what I said at the very beginning. None of us stays the same from one moment to the next. We change and our feelings change with us. We make choices as we move from moment to moment.

Some of these choices are conscious ones, some of them unconscious. In response to stress, difficulty and heavy demands, you can respond in one of many ways. The easier response may be the one you choose. However, in choosing it, you may be ducking a chance to grow, and by missing this chance, you may forfeit an opportunity to deepen the basis of the entire marriage relationship.

Do Babies Prevent Divorce?

Often, this question is asked. Or, you hear people say, "That couple would have stayed together if they had children." As a matter of fact, it is doubtful that the presence of a child can really serve to fortify a weak marriage, any more than it can threaten a truly strong marriage. The notion that babies solidify shaky homes is so widespread, I suspect, that many unhappy couples hope their problems will be solved by childbirth. Too often, they find they were wrong. I know of tragic cases where couples deliberately had children in an effort to hold their shaky marriages together. The inevitable divorce eventually followed, with the innocent youngster the real injured party.

Becoming Parents

Let's return to that typical young couple who have a baby a year or two after marriage and encounter a wide range of normal—and soluble—problems. Not too long after the baby arrives they may resume intercourse, unless there is some rare and unusual complication involving the wife.

When they resume their sexual relationship, should it be on the same "honeymoon basis" as before? Certainly not. The honeymoon is over. The couple must eventually mature into parents, or pay in serious consequences. In fact, the couple should not even hope for a return to the honeymoon aura of love-making and marital life in general. Why try to take a step backward only to remain in the same place?

Life has led our couple to a new stage. This is not a dreary fact, but a joyful one. Certainly, there are tensions in this new life stage. Overcoming them together is the essence of strengthening the marriage.

Husbands in this situation must go all out to understand their wives' anxieties about bodily changes, the future of the sex relationship, future pregnancies and many other vital factors. The husband must understand that his wife has doubts about her capabilities as a mother. Indeed, she may even be afraid to pick up the newborn infant for the first few days.

On the other hand, the wife must make a genuine effort to understand her husband's tensions, those likely to revolve around possible physical change in her, possible replacement of him by the baby in the wife's scale of affections and the other factors previously discussed.

I must repeat that tensions in this "first baby" period can be greatly lessened if the husband and wife can communicate their problems to each other *without* feeling weak or ashamed. They must be strong enough to lend each other support—this husband and wife who have taken the next big step in their marriage.

If they do these things—communicate openly and support each other, no one need ever wonder about them. No one need ever ask the question, "Were they really in love when they married?" This question really has no importance at all.

Far more important is the answer to this question: How do they feel about each other now, this day, this very minute?

12

Getting to Know Each Other

Complete sexual fulfillment in marriage cannot take place unless husband and wife really know each other. "But we *do* know each other!" the average married couple may exclaim. I wonder. Getting to know someone else—and yourself for that matter—takes effort. How *do* you get to know someone else?

The story is told of the great Russian writer, Boris Pasternak, who was being interviewed. When the interview was completed, a photographer came over to take pictures. Pasternak looked up wonderingly and said, "You wish to photograph me. But how can you make a good portrait of a person unless you know him well?"

When you stop to think about it, this is a penetrating question, the other side of which is that, as a great photographer once remarked to me, you can also know a person too well to photograph him. The reason is that when you know him that well, you no longer "see" him. In the last analysis, it is the eye behind the camera that must "see" a person, otherwise the camera will not "see" him either.

What has all this to do with marital compatibility and sexual fulfillment? Simply this. Many a married couple really do not know each other. They are aware of many surface tastes, likes, dislikes and reactions, but neither really knows what makes the other tick down deep inside. They have ceased "seeing" each other. Thus, many marriages lose their drive and undergo cycles that can almost be predicted.

The Cycles of Marriage

There is, at first, an early sense of newness. You are discovering your mate's surface attitudes and behavior patterns. He is discovering yours and the entire process is exciting. Then, gradually, the bloom comes off the rose. In a year, two, or three, many couples lose their sense of discovery. Their lives become routinized. They feel that they know their partners so well, and they fail to "see" them any more. Unless the couple sets about to take positive preventive measures, the marriage becomes simply an automatic matter with set habit patterns devoid of real meaning to one or both of those involved. In contrast, the next time you are with a couple who have been married eighteen or twenty years, but who have not lost the art of "seeing" each other, take the opportunity of observing them. Note their awareness and enjoyment of each other, the interchange of talk as if this were the first time each had met the other. You probably will feel that they are very lucky people and you will hope that some day your relationship with your mate can be as good. But are they merely lucky? Perhaps luck is an ingredient, but there's more to it.

Being Sure of Each Other

The husband and wife happily married for many years are likely to be sure of each other. Don't misunderstand. Neither can predict all the feelings or reactions of the other. Neither just takes the other for granted. But there is a range of common ground and a range of security that each derives from the other. Further, husband and wife gain comfort from feeling reasonably sure that the other will react in a mature, grown-up fashion to problems as they arise.

This comfort permeates the marriage. Its implications for sexual fulfillment are obvious. With husband and wife both open-minded, both flexible and both willing to please the other, sexual incompatibility is reduced to a minimum. The relaxed feeling of this type of marriage permeates every aspect of it.

Sharing, a Force for Good

Along with the comfort, security and relaxation, the happy marriage remains vital and dynamic. It is only natural that this vitality should spill over into the couple's sex life. The husband and wife are stimulatingly aware of each other. At parties, they do not escape into opposite corners, but, circulating freely, they meet periodically for a glance, a laugh, a touch. Clearly, they *are* husband and wife but also they "see" and "hear" each other. They connect, each delighting in the other's company.

This is not just a pose for the sake of convention or appearance, for they have long since been able to do without play-acting. Each one seems more joyful, more alive because of the other. And why not? When they first married, each thought the other the most wonderful person in the world. Neither expected this attitude to change with the years and it hasn't, for both took pains to keep this feeling going.

I cannot forget what one wonderfully happy couple told me after thirty-one years of marriage. "We have always found each other charming," the wife said, "and stimulating in a great many ways." The husband chimed in, "And we have always liked each other a great deal, as people, in addition to the love we feel and the physical satisfaction we share."

In just a few words, that couple had provided a revealing self-analysis that has ramifications for couples everywhere. They "liked" each other, as the husband said.

The Power of Friendship in Marriage

"Getting to know you, getting to know all about you. Getting to like you, getting to hope you like me . . ." These are words from a popular song in the play, *The King and I.* Lovers may wonder what these words have to do with them. The word "like," after all, is not often found in the vocabulary of lovers. Like denotes friendship, not love, they might say.

But liking is as vital to husband and wife as loving. Learning to like your partner is absolutely necessary to marriage. In all its aspects, the sexual one included, marriage should be based on friendship and companionship as well as on passion. Marriages sometimes flounder because it is much more difficult, at times, to like your partner than to love him or her. True friendship, lovers should always remember, is an art, and as with any art, friendship takes time to learn.

Many couples are in too great a hurry ever to come to know each other well enough to develop liking for each other. They are so anxious to achieve the ultimate relationship of marriage that they cheat themselves of the great experience of friendship before and during marriage. Not so a young couple I know, married a little more than eight years. Like all married couples, they have their emotional ups and downs, their financial problems, their happinesses and sorrows, but overall they are extremely happy.

In part, their happiness stems from their deep love. But there's something more. They realized early in their marriage the value of friendship—of "liking" one another. When the husband does something that profoundly dismays his wife (this happens in the happiest of marriages), she is likely to say something along these lines: "I love you as always, but I don't like you at all at this moment for what you have just done. . . ."

This type of remark has always served as a signal in their marriage. It triggers, almost invariably, a discussion of what the husband (or the wife for that matter) has done to disappoint the mate. The results are worth thinking about. The discussion clears the air—even if it has involved heated voices and charged emotions. Further, it serves to resolve the point at issue. In this way, the marriage is strengthened.

Why is this achieved? Because there is sufficient loving and "liking" along with generous amounts of mutual respect to carry this couple through the disagreement. They remain good friends throughout. I emphasize this because "bad friends" can feel love, passion, desire for one another and translate those qualities into a temporary compatibility.

The Power of Understanding in Marriage

After a while, the happy husband and wife learn how to react to what the other person *is* rather than to what he may do or say at a given moment. If you are such a spouse, you will have learned still more that is vital in marriage. You will have learned that your fundamental feeling of friendship and liking can carry you through moments when your partner is downright disagreeable, silly, unattractive, disgusting, or a complete failure in life.

Knowing the power of understanding and the power of friendship in marriage, many authorities advise against early marriages. Divorce statistics bolster the advice. There are more divorces of couples who marry under the age of eighteen than over the age of eighteen. Obviously, the younger couples have failed to allow themselves sufficient time to become real friends with each other. Obviously, too, the deep, insightful understanding that is necessary to sustain marriage has not had time to be developed in our teen-agers.

Three Ways to Marital Understanding

Once married, how can you begin to know your partner? The surface attitudes require no discovery, for these emerge quickly for you to understand. I am talking about the deep-down values —the ones that come to light in moments of stress, when everything in the marriage does not go the way you thought it would. Inevitably, there will be some of these moments in regard to the physical love of marriage.

First of all, the human heart is shy of opening its innermost corners when there is fear of being hurt. This means simply that if you want to know a person and know him well, he must be sure that you do not want to hurt him in any way.

What is likely to create such a fear? A habitually sharp tongue can do it. Continuous mockery of others or of self can do it. Dishonesty in simple human relationships can also lead to this type of fear. So can expressions of hatred, lust, greed, jealousy, envy and insecurity. If, instinctively or otherwise, your mate discovers that your first concern is yourself, the underpinnings of your marriage are bound to become shaky. Love and fear do not mix well together. To know each other fully, neither partner must have reason to fear the other.

Second, *you* must make the first gesture of "liking" and of loving. You must be *for* your partner. Friendship between two people never springs full-blown from a single moment. It is the result of many moments through the years, of warmth, of support, of loyalty and of genuine concern each for the other.

This is especially important to remember in times of stress caused by bad times or by the anticipation of bad times. Whoever first thought of the phrase, "when the chips are down," was correct. It is when the chips are down that a fellow really needs a friend. It's also the moment when a fellow finds out what kind of a friend the other person is. In no aspect of living is this more important than in marriage.

Third, in true friendship, the other person gains a sense that you value him for himself, not for what he can do for you. One of the greatest things we can do in this life is to give other people a sense of their own worth in *our* eyes. Once again, this is part of the ability to "see" in marriage. It has magnificent powers in all phases of marriage. In the sexuality of marriage, it helps immeasurably in maintaining mutual respect and admiration which leads to sexual fulfillment.

When husbands and wives act toward each other as if the other was valueless, they erode the foundations of their marriage. They decrease their loving and liking; they rouse feelings of frustration and failure that sooner or later may become the predominating tone of the marriage itself. With such a tone, there is not likely to be a release from sexual tensions, but rather a deepening of them. Mutual trust and respect are the antidotes.

But, say the young married couple in love, we aren't interested in friendship. We're interested in love and love-making.

Everything will fall into place when we experience passion together. *Nonsense.*

To sustain a marriage over the long haul, loving and liking must go together. Love without friendship is like icing without cake. A little bit is fine. Too much alone provides nothing of real substance. Ask anyone who has been married happily for ten years or longer. He will tell you that plenty of practice in the art of friendship provides a head start toward successful marriage.

Getting to Know Myself

It might seem surprising to discuss "getting to know myself" after "getting to know you." It might seem that getting to know another person should come *after* one understands oneself and not before. I doubt it.

"Getting to know myself" is one of the most difficult things in the world to do. Not only is it tough to accomplish, it is even tough to start doing. People shy away from it because they have a feeling that they will not like what they discover. In addition, the incentive for getting to know oneself must come from outside oneself. It is far more likely to be the result of stresses and strains in life than of easy living.

Marriage As Stress

Whether or not we like the idea, marriage involves some basic stresses. I know a young man twice married and twice divorced who admits readily that he cannot withstand the stresses of marital responsibility. It places real demands upon us, sometimes involving sorrow and pain. This is inevitable. Even the most harmonious marriage has difficult moments, moments in which we must decide which comes first, the marriage or "myself." This is why I have postponed a discussion of "getting to know myself." I believe the real stimulus for that is "getting to know you."

When Boris Pasternak refused the Nobel Prize he told his friends, "This and much else is hard and sad. But it is these fatalities that give life weight and depth and gravity and make it extraordinary, rapturous, magical and real." His conviction is borne out in all our daily living.

Have you ever seen a photographic print made from an underexposed negative? The outlines of the picture are extremely thin because there is little or no shadowing. Everything is light and shallow, without depth or roundness. Thus, everything in the photo loses its real meaning.

If there had been the proper exposure, shadows would appear. The dark would fill spaces, marking contrasts with the brilliant play of light. I think this is what Pasternak meant with regard to living. If you give yourself to life fully and deeply, plunging yourself into it with all your heart, you will not be able to escape dark, shadowing experiences, some of them difficult and tragic, others stressful and disturbing. Still others will bring ultimate joy. You will be living life in the round, and from the more painful experiences will come knowledge of your own capacities as a human being. You will learn how and why you cope with situations, live with them, accept or reject them. Out of this knowledge of your capacities will come increasing strength for whatever else may await you around the corner, increasing sureness of your ability to meet it.

The individual who lives a fluffy cotton existence has no way to determine how he will measure up in the tough spots. He has no way of judging whether he has the capacity to be strong enough to meet demands that may be made upon him. In short, he has no basis for measuring the kind of person he really is.

This must frighten him more than a little. He must be insecure because he is a mystery—even to himself.

Sex, the Hub of Marriage

The person who has not attempted some self-assessment from time to time is a bad marital risk. For marriage consists not of one, but of many demands, some light, some heavy, some trivial, some profoundly important. Like the radiating spokes of a wheel, most of these demands spring from and return to the hub of the marriage itself. This hub is the sexual relationship.

Attitudes, values, decision-making and most other aspects of marriage are colored by the climate of marital sex. Even money problems can become related to sex. A young husband who feels unsure of himself and whose masculinity is threatened because he cannot seem to help his wife respond to him, unconsciously may try to bolster his masculinity by using finances as a club in the relationship with his wife. This is one reason why "getting to know myself" is so important. Meeting difficulties head-on is much more constructive than attempting to avoid them. In meeting them, we discover how we measure up ourselves.

In the song from *The King and I,* the words, "getting to hope you like me," foreshadow the unexpressed feeling, "getting to hope that *I* like me." You want to like yourself, so that you can be really free to like other people. It is obvious that you will not be able to like yourself until you know yourself pretty well. If you fail to know yourself well, the chances for sexual happiness in marriage are decreased greatly.

One Road to Sexual Happiness

We all know people who impress us with their quiet sense of power. They seem to have infinite capacity for doing things.

They are not frightened or stampeded by life, by difficulties, by tragedies, by marriage, by the challenges that marriage entails. They seem so stable and so sure that it seems as if nothing could upset them. They appear to have made a great peace between themselves, the world, God and the demands that are made upon them.

We are apt to envy these people, but there isn't one of us who could not approach the same state of stability and deep satisfaction. Within each of us there are the resources. The key question is, will we find them and use them?

If we stop to analyze why we feel almost instinctively that these people whom we admire as strong and to be counted upon, know themselves, like themselves and do not shortchange the relationships closest to them, we must conclude that they know how to live with the greatest satisfaction for themselves.

Having made a great effort and having succeeded in understanding themselves—and having come to terms with the personal demands made on them—they then manage to live for others and at the same time live for themselves. These people stand in strong contrast to those you may know who constantly "sacrifice" themselves—or claim they do—for their loved ones. For sacrifice that is felt as sacrifice can be destructive. It reduces in stature the person who makes the sacrifice and it is liable to cause resentment and guilt on the part of the person receiving the sacrifice.

In a *McCall's* magazine article of a few years ago, John K. Lagemann said, "The greatest gift we can make to our loved ones is the gift of ourselves and the more we sacrifice ourselves, the less we have to give. The healthy self-love of people who invest in their own greater capacity for living is always reflected in the greater happiness they bring to others. . . ." This simply means that each of us must examine very carefully what the word "happiness" really means to him. Each of us must determine how much of giving and how much of receiving is essential to our true happiness.

How does all this relate to sexual tension in marriage? Here's how. The person who is not well along the road to understanding and liking himself, who considers that his bargain with life is poorly made, who is ill-at-ease and suspects that he is inadequate—this person will expect sex to compensate for all of the deficiencies in his life. But it cannot, and he and his partner will be tragically disappointed if they expect that it will.

Perhaps this person of whom we are speaking will be so restless and dissatisfied that he finds he cannot respond in sex at all, or give particular pleasure to his mate. Full sexual responsiveness in marriage comes to people who are at peace with themselves and with each other, at peace in a growing, dynamic way, not in a deadly dull way.

Sex responsiveness comes to those who not only view sex as a sacred and cherished factor in living, but who also retain good perspective about it by being sensitive to the needs of their partners and by taking into account the warmth, graciousness and humor inherent in successful marital sex.

Sex does not depend for its deepest satisfaction on the selfish pleasure of the moment. It is the outgrowth of living for oneself—by living for the beloved.

13

"Doctor, My Husband Says I'm Frigid . . ."

How often I have heard these words, either directly or by letter. They come from women desperate from a sense of failure in the relationship that is most important to their lives. Some of these women wonder what orgasm is, never having experienced one. Others do so occasionally, but with difficulty, and the difficulty increases as their anxiety about it increases.

Almost all such women feel that they are missing something vital to their lives. Either their husbands have told them so, or they have read considerably on the subject, or other women have related the wonders of their own experience. At any rate, the woman who rarely if ever experiences orgasm feels unfulfilled—and rightly so.

When a woman tells me that this is her problem, I ask a good many questions. At times, I get an adequate explanation, at other times, I get no answers that are helpful. At any rate, I fit in what the woman says about herself with information from similar cases, and I form a mental picture of what must have happened to her to make her unable to respond as her body was meant to respond.

Are Husbands to Blame for "Frigidity"?

Some of you reading these pages may, at one time or another, have been called frigid. A good deal has been written about so-called frigidity. Much of the blame has been laid to the poor approach and techniques of the husband. In some cases, I suppose this is so.

However, as I have indicated, love is not a matter of tricks and techniques. Other factors are usually at work. These factors have little to do with what the husband does or says, his approach in love-making or his attitudes toward it. They usually stem from the woman herself, and particularly from the woman's upbringing.

Why Some Women Think They're Frigid

Conditioning from birth is the factor which most often results in a woman's believing she is frigid. There are many experiences in childhood that can make a woman block off and forget sex later on. At times, these experiences will result in extremely unhealthy emotions concerning the entire subject of sex. They make young women put the brakes on sexual desire, experience and satisfaction. For such young women, there is a climate of fear, insecurity and dread concerning the whole subject of sex, and these are the women who may be branded as frigid at one time or another in their lives.

Overcoming Feelings of Frigidity

Remember I said that your past experiences make a sort of mental and emotional film of your life. It would be wonderful, of course, if you could really treat your life as if it were a film. If you could reverse the film, run it backward, so to speak, the way we rewind film, and then cut, edit and do retakes on all the big and little experiences that shaped your attitudes toward sex, this would be a truly helpful miracle to accomplish.

The happy result of this would be you, just as you are now, but with one big difference: You would have a warm, natural, happy and comfortable feeling about sex. It's not impossible to do, and I know of several women who have gone far toward solving their sexual problems by "rewinding" and observing their own life's film. They were sensitive to the need to help themselves and their husbands, and they accomplished the task pretty much by themselves.

There was the case of Ann, aged twenty-four when she married. Ann had been told over and over by her parents that "nice girls" did not permit boys to touch them—ever. All during her dating and courtship years, she followed her parents' rigid advice. No boy had ever even kissed her. Whenever one tried, she stiffened up, resisted and often broke into tears. Usually the boy became disgusted and left her alone thereafter. When Ann married, therefore, she felt she was "completely pure."

When, in the normal course of events, her husband tried to make love to her, the experience was so strange and so alien to her, that she was utterly unable to respond. She balked at his love-making, telling him she was especially shy. Weeks of this sort of thing stretched into months and Ann's husband, understandably, became desperate.

One day, she broke down and told him of her rigid upbringing and of the "no sexual play" edict that she had followed so religiously. Fortunately, Ann's husband was understanding and patient. He got her to talk about her past experiences, about her parents' rigidity and her own feelings about it. Then, slowly, he began to explore her body—with her. Sensitive to her needs, he did not rush things. Intercourse at first was painful and repugnant to her.

Gradually, however, Ann came to understand the root of her difficulty. Gradually, she accepted more and more of her husband's love-making. Certainly, there were tense moments. Certainly, there were tears on Ann's part and disappointment mingled with joy on both their parts. But in a little more than a year, Ann and her husband were progressing well toward a full and genuinely rewarding sexual life together. Her genuine desire to edit the film of her early experience was the catalytic agent that brought success.

Alice was twenty-six when she married. In her home, there were no restrictions similar to those in the previous case. She did not have intercourse prior to marriage, but she became excited by the thought of intercourse, with all its concomitants, and waited eagerly for the opportunity. When Alice was twenty-four, she became engaged. She believed she was deeply in love. Her fiancé and she had feverish necking and petting sessions, but she was consistent in her refusal to have intercourse before marriage.

Two weeks before the scheduled nuptials were to take place, Alice's fiancé convinced her that they ought to discover each other sexually before marriage as a sort of "insurance" that all would go well in the marriage. Alice was reluctant at first, but later agreed with some misgivings, as has many another girl faced with the same decision.

As the moment approached, Alice panicked. She really was unready for intercourse at this stage in the relationship, but she feared that if she did not give in, her fiancé would think less of her and perhaps leave her altogether. In the end, she was completely unable to respond, and the more her fiancé tried to arouse her, the less she wanted him. At the moment of actual intercourse, she began to cry with fear and guilt. Her fiancé forced her and the pain she felt emotionally expressed itself physically.

She cried out in anguish. Her fiancé reached orgasm prematurely, soiled the bedclothes and both of them were deeply disgusted by the entire ordeal. The fiancé was so distraught, as a matter of fact, that he refused to marry her. Looking back on the experience, of course, Alice thought that the broken engagement was all for the best. She came to view her ex-fiancé as an immature and inadequate person.

Two years later, she married another young man, but even then she could not bring herself to respond fully to him. He enjoyed intercourse, but she did not. This made her husband feel inadequate and guilty and he sought the reason for her lack of response. Alice faced a dilemma. Should she tell or shouldn't she? She summoned her courage and decided to risk the mature gesture. She decided to rerun the film of her single previous experience.

Her husband understood fully. As the months went on, he helped Alice, gently but persuasively, to forget the previous experience and to begin to live the present one vigorously and without fear. His patience was rewarded. In a matter of months, Alice looked on herself and her body with more understanding and began to feel that sex with her husband—the man she truly loved—not only could not be wrong or unclean in any of its manifestations, but was actually a joy that would permeate their entire life together. You may think to yourself that time really healed this particular wound. Perhaps it did. But time alone could not have done it; it needed also Alice's own courage as well as a devoted, aware and emotionally mature husband.

The Feelings of Unresponsive Women

Of course, many women fail to run back their memory film. They refuse to think deeply about themselves or to spend time in self-analysis. As a result, they do not find their way to release from sexual tensions. What reservations and anxieties do such women feel? These can be classified because they are universal, just as the solutions are universal.

"This is a part of my body that must never be touched, by me or by anyone else." That is one typical unconscious conviction of the unresponsive female. "This is really a bad and dirty thing." "Why must I endure this? Solely for the pleasure of my husband?" "Why am I a woman—and have no control over the sexual aggression committed on my body?" All these and many more are thoughts which occur to the unresponsive woman.

In addition, there are feelings of chagrin and disappointment. "What's so wonderful about this?" she asks herself. "It's not like the books say at all! It's not ecstasy." "It's really quite uncomfortable." And there are still other feelings that intrude: "He's starting, now. Oh, dear." "He's taking all the covers off." "The sheet is wrinkled; it's uncomfortable." "It's too hot, I hate getting all sweaty." "That light bothers me. Why can't he turn it off. . . ." "Someone will hear us." "He doesn't care about me, he's concerned only with his own pleasure. . . ." "He did it last night. Does he have to do it *every* night?" "I'll never get my rest. . . ."

Now take a deep breath and sit back. How many of those sentences produced a flash of recognition in you? How many times did you say, "That's the way *I* feel." Once? Twice? Several times?

Then you are a great deal like many other troubled women, but that does not mean that you are frigid. It means that in order to free yourself from these blocks to sexual response, you must do some re-editing of your own life's film. You must try and do for yourself what a psychiatrist helps a really sick person do: re-examine and change some of the attitudes you *know* you have, some that you sometimes *think* you have, and discover and change some you aren't even aware you have.

How to Right the Wrongs

First, you must return in your mind to when you were a little girl. What do you remember about the sex instruction that you received? As you recall bits and pieces of it, try to redirect your thinking and your attitudes about these past events.

For instance, can you remember once when your mother "caught" you playing with yourself in the genital region? This must have happened at least once—it is such a common occurrence. Do you remember how you were feeling before she saw you? Didn't it feel warm and comfortable? Didn't you have a lovely sensation while playing with yourself? Try to recapture the actual feeling, try to feel that way now.

Psychologists and other qualified persons tell us that it is perfectly normal to feel that way. Further, they tell us that *all* —and I repeat *all*—children play with themselves at one time or another. Now try to remember back to that moment when your mother caught you.

Did you feel a stunned surprise at her onslaught? Did she scold you? Did she slap your hands or perhaps threaten to cut them off? (Hard to believe, isn't it? But some mothers have done this.) Did she tell you that you were a bad, dirty girl and God would punish you? Did she say or imply that if you persisted in "playing with yourself" you might become insane?

Remember, our mothers were conditioned by their mothers to believe these things, so your mother was not trying to be cruel to you, but was full of genuine concern and fear for you. She *believed* what she said, and she was trying to protect you for the future. But we now know that that way was the wrong way.

How did you react after you had been detected and threatened in this way? As you unwind the film of your memory, probably you will discover that you did one of two things. One: You secretly kept right on playing with yourself, because it was so pleasurable that it was stronger than your fears, but taking great care not to be rediscovered. As a result of the whole occurrence, you carried along with you, for the rest of your life, the conviction that this was a bad, dirty and wrong thing. Thus, your sense of guilt at your conduct and fear of its consequences probably has haunted you to this very instant and is one of the main causes of the inhibition of your normal sex instincts.

The second way in which you might have reacted is somewhat different. Instead of secretly persisting in this type of sexual play, you may have erased the whole thing completely from your memory. As of today, the whole episode may be so buried that you are one of those women who quite honestly believe that they have never played with their genitals in their lives and have never had any kind of feeling there—much less a pleasurable one.

Now, wind back the film to the original incident and run through it again. Even if you cannot remember it, try to imagine it because it or something similar must have happened. Let's pretend your mother had not been conditioned by her mother to have fear and to feel guilt concerning masturbation. Pretend that when she "caught" you, she wisely did nothing, or perhaps took you on her knee and cuddled you, thus providing what you really needed, namely a feeling that she was kind and strong and not angry with you but loved you very much. Can you now re-edit this moment in the film of your life?

Can you recapture the lovely feeling of warmth and pleasure that you experienced when you were playing with yourself? Then go on from there to feel as if you were being held comfortably in your mother's arms. This could lead to the feeling that what you were doing was as warm, lovely, comfortable and *right* as the feeling of her arms about you.

Continue reviewing your film. At each moment when you remember feeling fear and guilt about playing with yourself, try to erase this feeling and to substitute instead that feeling of warmth and comfort, that it is *all right,* that it is part of life, a good and normal part. If you can do this, you are on the road to improvement. If you can erase the feeling of guilt and connect the feeling of warmth, comfort and rightness to that special part of your body, you will have taken the first important step toward a happier sex life with your husband.

The Feeling That Men Are Bad

Remember, if you can, another event that almost certainly took place in your youth because it has happened to nearly all of us.

Remember when a little boy was "caught" lifting your skirt and touching you? Was there a terrible outcry? A scene? Was your father called in? The boy's parents? Police, perhaps? Were there threats from all sides? What do you remember most vividly? The fuss and loud, angry voices and strange, disturbed look on the faces of your parents, or the simple, innocent little act that caused it all? And afterward, were you filled with a strong feeling that boys were dirty beasts, dangerous to be with? Did this feeling persist? It does in countless young women.

Ask yourself still more questions. If the feeling about the "bestiality" of boys persisted in you, did you have to make a very conscious exception with regard to your own father, brother and, later, with regard to your fiancé? On your honeymoon, did these inner feelings and memories not rise up and almost choke you so that at times you felt that this man, your husband, must also be one of those "dirty beasts"? Didn't your feeling regarding the sex act itself make you believe that here was something dangerous, unpleasant and bad all rolled into one?

Now, return to your re-editing job. Go back to the place in your memory film where you and the little boy were playing before you were discovered. How did you feel then? Wasn't it pleasurable? Wasn't it exciting? Weren't you somewhat aroused sexually?

Now, try to erase all the loudness and ugliness of the scene that followed. Call upon your inner resources, common sense, hope and strength to realize that the way you felt with the little boy is exactly the way you should be feeling now in your sexual relations with your husband—filled with a sense of discovery, of excitement, of pleasure. Try to believe that if the unpleasant reactions had not intervened, you *would* feel that way now. You would have no trouble responding to your husband, but would have truly pleasurable sex with him, and would happily experience orgasm.

The famous anthropologist Margaret Mead has made extensive studies of various civilizations in all parts of the world. She has found several where the very normal sex play of little children, as I have discussed it above, is not punished. No one remarks about it. Girls grow up with a genuine feeling that their sex organs are a source of warm, personal comfort and pleasure. When they reach adulthood, these girls are perfectly capable of giving free and normal expression to their love for their husbands.

The "Sexless" Woman

What about the woman who says—and honestly believes—that she has never felt a sex impulse in her life? Undoubtedly, this woman led a sheltered and restricted early life. Her mother, father or both repressed all sex experience. They may have refused even to discuss it. If this woman ever received sex information from her parents, it was on a cold, unemotional level. Most likely, it stressed the reproductive act, never the act of love.

Or else, in providing information, the parents tinged the whole thing with their own deeply felt emotion that the sex act was dirty, immoral or unpleasant. The result may be a woman who feels absolutely incapable of any sexual feeling.

If you feel like such a woman, you have an extremely difficult job to do. For you may not even have conscious memories that can be altered and improved by re-editing the film of early experience.

Rediscover Your Body

No matter what the cause of your difficulty, there is one step more for you to take. You must make the bridge between what your conscious mind has forgotten but your body has not. Waiting to be reawakened are the feelings that were so carefully put to sleep by your conditioning and experience so many years ago. Waiting to be accomplished is the normal discovery of your own body that was frustrated too early in your life.

You yourself must reawaken your body, rediscover it, reeducate it. You yourself, with the help of your husband, must continue the exploration that was interrupted years ago. Find out for yourself how it feels to touch yourself in certain places. Find out which places arouse most pleasure in you when touched. Communicate these discoveries to your husband.

Be patient with yourself. Take time to arrive at the realization that not a single place on or within your body is dangerous or "dirty" to touch, nor can any gentle and loving means of stimulation ever be "bad" or cause harm. Hold fast to the thought that great religious leaders assure you that this portion of your body was made not only to procreate, but to be the exquisite instrument of the act of love between your husband and yourself.

It will help, too, if you become aware of your husband's body and learn that it is to be loved, not feared or found distasteful. You should discover for yourself that seminal fluid, far from being unclean, is odorless and tasteless. The small amount of such fluid ejaculated at intercourse, perhaps a teaspoonful, is no reason for feeling soiled. Nor is it a reason for resorting to immediate cleansing, as so many women feel they must do.

Interruption to Normal Sexual Response

Sometimes a woman has had a normal sexual response until something throws her off. Pregnancy before marriage may do this. So may the following: induced abortion, either in or out of marriage; criminal assault; birth of an abnormal child; death of a fiancé; being deserted; or a wide range of serious emotional problems, such as deep-seated depression and anxiety.

It is obvious, when a woman has gone from normal response to little or no response, that she is in need of professional help.

The family physician can be called in and often, I suspect, it would be wise to see a psychiatrist or some other professional with psychiatric training.

Are There Really Frigid Women?

By now, you can realize how important it is to understand the true, underlying feelings that you have about sex and how they came about. When you have managed to analyze and focus these feelings, when you have lost your sense of fear and guilt, when that part of your body no longer seems unknown and unclean, when you have learned by your memory film re-editing and experimentation to reawaken your inborn capacity to feel sexually, you and your husband can begin the long and happy experience of working out a normal sex life together.

Many women can do a complete job of memory re-editing by themselves, but an understanding husband is of untold help both in bringing the problem out in the open and in its resolution. Some women, however, cannot do a complete self-analysis. They may require psychiatric help from a marriage counselor or other professional.

It is tragic that small occurrences in our childhood and early formative years can have so devastating an effect on our later lives. But it is wonderful to remember that we can really get over these ill effects and become fully capable in the essential relationship of marriage.

Does this last remark apply to the so-called "frigid woman"? Yes, indeed. For the term itself is inaccurate. There are hardly any truly frigid women.

Down deep within the overwhelming majority is a sexual need and capacity for fulfillment that awaits only liberation.

14

Divorced or Widowed

There comes in the course of some lives a moment that inevitably is awful and frightening. It is the moment when, after years that may have been happy and satisfying, the marriage comes to an end, either through death or divorce.

In divorce, authorities tell us, at least one-third of the cases can be placed at the doorstep of sexual problems, or sexual unhappinesses that ultimately manifest themselves in other phases of the marriage. In cases of death, of course, there are different factors. Perhaps you were extremely happy when death intervened. Or perhaps you were unhappy with your mate, whose subsequent death may thus leave you struggling with a guilt-ridden sense of relief.

For whatever reason, the fact is that now you are alone and the aloneness is accentuated because you are not used to it. You are accustomed to being one of two people linked very closely together. This aloneness, sought for or thrust upon you, has two faces. One you turn toward the world. The other you turn inward toward yourself. The latter face probes deeply into your inner being when you are by yourself.

However, the face you turn toward the world may be a fairly artificial one. Because you may have children to consider, it is extremely important to you that you remain unchanged—in their eyes—as a result of what has happened. Thus, you will "carry on" in front of them, maintaining the household as smoothly as possible in this trying time of your life.

The same holds for your friends, except for a very few before whom you may be free to show what you really feel. As for casual acquaintances, there are always the ones who say quite easily, "He (or she) really is taking it very well."

The Need to Remarry

What of the other face, the face seen very dimly even by oneself? This is the face you may be reluctant to acknowledge even to yourself. Almost inevitably, this face consciously or unconsciously begins to prepare for the next marriage.

Shocking, you say. I disagree. Stop and think how natural a second marriage really is, especially if the first one was happy. A truly well-founded second marriage certainly can decrease sexual tensions. It can provide an equilibrium for children where equilibrium is lacking. Further, it can profit by the mistakes of the previous marriage.

There are some who say that the highest compliment you can pay your deceased mate is to marry shortly after the loss. This may or may not be true. It does follow, however, that most persons who have known a happy and rewarding marriage will seek to replace it when it is lost. The same applies to the person who is divorced. Even in a tumultuous marriage there must have been some joyous moments. It is perfectly normal to want to enlarge on such moments in a second marriage.

For the unmistakable fact is that man and woman were not meant to live without each other. Many do live alone, of course, and satisfactorily, too. Others find loving companionship through life with members of their own sex. But for most men and women the fundamental drive is toward each other. This drive should regain momentum very soon after the break in a marriage.

Can a Second Marriage Produce Full Sexuality?

I must answer "yes" to this question, if for no other reason than the fact that second marriages have so often proven eminently successful in every regard. Of course, there are doubts that sex will be "as good" with a second mate. These are almost inevitable.

But the experience of many couples provides sound evidence that second-marriage sexuality can be even better than first. Let me cite the case of one young woman I know. Doris was twenty-three when she first married. She was, of course, inexperienced sexually and somewhat afraid of the entire subject. Her first husband was strange, moody, abstracted and little concerned with anything beyond his artistic interests.

Sex, to him, was an obligation and not too attractive a one at that. Doris's introduction to marital sex was thus an unpleasant one. In a short time, the marriage started to crumble. Neither was well suited to the other and both realized it.

They were divorced and Doris remarried. Her second husband is a forthright, no-nonsense individual who, nonetheless, is extremely patient with his wife. He understands that he must help undo Doris's squeamish and insecure feelings. Doris and her second husband have been married more than five years and thus far they are making a fine sexual adjustment to each other.

The case of Rhoda, aged twenty-six, is still another example. Her first husband was a latent homosexual, uninterested in Rhoda or any other woman. She remarried, this time to a disturbed young man who ultimately deserted her. Rhoda's immaturity had made her unable to choose the right mate. Her third marriage, however, has worked out very well. The trauma of the earlier marriages has not been blotted out altogether, but recently Rhoda told me that she and her husband made a good sexual adjustment within the first year of marriage. They have been married now for four years and have two children.

The Need for Discretion

I do not mean to imply by what I have said previously that a divorced or widowed person should openly venture forth and flaunt his efforts to find a new mate. Far from it. Rather the drive in this direction should take the form of expending effort to heal oneself from the wound. In short, you seek to make yourself a whole person again, a person in your own right, after having lived as part of another person for a long time.

Psychiatrists tell us that after any loss, particularly through death, it is vital that plenty of time be taken to become completely aware of the loss in every phase of one's life with the beloved mate, to relive these phases consciously, not in order to push them away but in order to become thoroughly convinced that the mate is gone forever, and in this slow, inescapable and painful process, to allow full expression to the grief that is inevitable and true. The old saying, "Cry it out, it will do you good," has scientific basis here, and this is why time and plenty of it are needed to accomplish this adjustment to loss.

In the process, you must try to find out about yourself (once again, rerun the memory film) by assessing your real needs and desires. You should seek to evaluate what you have to offer a new marriage, why the old marriage failed, if it did. In addition, you should think long and hard about the qualities that you really want in a new mate.

Remember, you have had the experience of a marriage, whether it was dissolved by intent or by death. Thus, you are no longer a complete novice on the subject. You know some of the ingredients for success; you should know, too, some of the pitfalls. You should also by now be aware of some of your own weaknesses and strengths.

As you begin to reassemble the pieces of your life, thoughts of self-evaluation should be going through your mind. For some, the readjustment period may be brief—not longer than a few months. For others, it will take a good deal longer. As time passes, you should let your instinctive drive toward remarriage develop naturally.

Aloneness—Other Readjustments

The person alone is suddenly faced with a great many new decisions. Some have to do with money, the children if any, the house, furniture and earning a living. If you are a woman, you may not be familiar with the financial and breadwinning aspects. If you are a man, the household and offspring problems are the ones with which you are not totally familiar.

However, the decisions press in on you. Family and friends may help, but the great portion of the burden rests upon your own shoulders. You are carrying all the responsibility now.

Then there is the question of social life. If you are a man, it is much easier, of course, to resume some semblance of normal social activity, to pick up the telephone and seek out your own dates. But if you are a woman, accustomed to being escorted and to having your evenings planned for you, it can be extremely difficult.

If you have just been divorced, you will shrink from having your friends think that you "are on the prowl," even though you know deep down that you really are. If you are recently widowed, you will have a gnawing feeling of discomfort that comes with imposing one's grief on others. Certainly, you will shrink from the possible accusation of others that you are already "looking for someone else." Therefore, for a woman, resumption of social life is not easy unless you have good friends who remember to invite you out, even though there is the problem of finding the "extra man."

Facing the Empty Bed

When you do return from an evening out, what about your inner feelings, the deep ones that are difficult to admit, even to yourself? Inevitably, these revolve around that terrible moment when you go into your bedroom alone and shut the door.

You look at the bed and you realize all over again that the person with whom you shared that bed has gone irrevocably from your life. No matter if the loss was from divorce or death, this can be a shattering moment and one that must be faced every night when you enter that room.

What happens then? The answer is vital to your present and future.

There are some people, not strong people, who will do anything in the world, quite literally, to avoid facing that empty room. They will fill their activities—and ultimately, their beds

—with people who are of no real consequence to them, simply because they cannot bear the emptiness. By doing this, they are actually being self-destructive. They retard the moment when another suitable mate might be found. There is too much hubbub, too much confusion, too many people in their lives. There is insufficient time, peace and silence to allow a worthwhile, new relationship to develop.

Such a state of affairs can end tragically. One divorcée I know embarked on long and involved affairs with two men over a four-year period. With each, she deluded herself into believing that having intercourse was the only way to "catch" a new husband. The men involved were both opportunistic and irresponsible. Their attitude was "If I can go to bed with her when I like, why get married?" —an extremely common attitude of men who prey on the divorced and widowed woman.

There are other separated persons, stronger, or perhaps more fearful of chastisement, who keep their lives and bedrooms empty for many months or years. They give themselves more than adequate time for healing, for self-analysis and understanding, and for new relationships to develop.

Perhaps out of fear, they never quite plunge into a new relationship. They hold back, and if they do this for too long a period, they may end up alone and feeling cheated. Perhaps this group is the most tragic of all, for their reluctance to act deprives them of real happiness.

I know a thirty-six-year-old divorced woman who was on the brink of a new marriage. She felt deeply that her two children, aged nine and five, should have a father, and she had great confidence in her selection of a second partner. Suddenly, for reasons that still are not clear to her, she broke off with her fiancé. For weeks, she went around in a fog, not quite understanding why she had done what she had done.

Finally, a friend convinced her that she had cheated herself and her children out of a potentially good life with this man.

Her friend convinced her, too, that she needed outside help. Because this divorcée had great respect and affection for her minister, she consulted him. He is helping her to understand that a second marriage can be a happy arrangement for all concerned.

I mention this case history to stress one point. The period when one is alone can be exceedingly difficult without friends. Here friendship can be invaluable to help ease this period of seeking and trial. One may need to call on one's friends, to impose on them, to beg for help, understanding and love which you know they can give out of the richness of their own good lives. You, the person now alone who is not accustomed to aloneness, need the love of friends to tide you over until you have found your own love.

Sex After a Broken Marriage

What happens to one's sexual appetite after the marriage has been broken for one reason or another? I suppose there are as many answers as there are people. Generally, the answers differ considerably for men and for women, although some men and some women will find the same answer: "Live it up. Don't spend a moment alone. Anyone will do." This is an extreme but all too common solution.

For the greatest number of people, the answer is not as definite. How does one live with normal sexual tension after a married life which has permitted its periodic release?

Putting aside those people who find the answer in aggressive and resentful promiscuity, there are, I think, several other main groups. One becomes sexually neutral and, as a result, suffers for the duration of its aloneness. Another group seeks honestly to find a new partner, acting with restraint, good taste, but with expressions of love that seem appropriate to them during the quest. A sexual relationship set up by an individual of this group is far removed from those of the "live-it-up" group, because it is not keyed primarily to sex, but rather to an honest, one-at-a-time, person-to-person relationship that may ultimately prove to be the one sought.

What this second group attempts to do is entirely normal, entirely consistent with the dictates of conscience and with the realities of the situation. It should be stressed, however, that in searching for a new partner, good taste and care for the feelings of others must dominate, for a deeply involved relationship becoming obvious too soon after the first marriage has dissolved may be emotionally upsetting to children who have reached the age of awareness. Discretion must be used and time allowed to permit the flowering of the new relationship in a natural way and without shock to anyone intimately concerned.

There is still a third group. For a variety of reasons, these people are not ready or able to develop a new, meaningful relationship. Therefore they find some sexual relief in masturbation. This may or may not be accompanied by a sense of guilt, which may, in turn, depend partly on how well these people were able to adjust to sex in their initial marriages.

Masturbation After a Broken Marriage

First, I would like to stress that masturbation can never serve as a substitute for a meaningful relationship for the divorced or widowed. At best, it can only serve those realistic individuals who recognize it for what it is: a stopgap measure toward some relief from sexual tension. It should not obscure the ultimate goal for divorced or widowed persons, namely a new partner who can give and receive genuine love.

I have stressed that masturbation is not physically harmful, although it may have an emotionally destructive effect if it is not fully understood. Handed from generation to generation has been a fear almost amounting to horror of anything having to do with sexual activity in children. And, of course, masturbation usually is the first childhood sexual activity. I believe the following facts bear repeating in the present context of the divorced or widowed person.

Ordinarily, children discover the pleasurable sensation of masturbation at about age two or three, sometimes a little earlier, sometimes a little later. Youngsters are soon made aware that this activity is not acceptable. Thus, it proceeds fairly privately and usually not too actively until the age of seven or eight. At this age, it is apt to cease almost completely, as this is when children's interests are drawn constantly outward—from themselves. Boys become involved in gangs, girls become intensely interested in a wide variety of group activities. Furthermore, around this age psychiatrists tell us, young human beings go into what is called a quiescent, or sexually neutral, phase.

Around the age of twelve or thirteen, puberty begins. The young body undergoes the changes associated with sexual maturation. The sex organs begin to produce an increasing amount of the sex hormones. Visible changes in the body contours, the breasts, the distribution of hair and size of the sex organs themselves begin to take place.

At this point, the young person becomes increasingly aware of feelings of sexuality and increasingly sensitive to the dynamic bodily alterations taking place. At this time, too, the young person is particularly susceptible to fears, guilt and uncertainties. If the adults closest to him multiply his fears and uncertainties regarding his bodily cravings, his life will be a good deal more difficult than it need be. Thus, most psychiatrists advise that parents pay no attention if they do note evidence of masturbation. Rather the parents should concentrate on having an excellent relationship with their children. They should see to it that the children have many outlets for their interests and energies, but that demands and pressures not be laid too heavily upon them, for the child whose parents expect too much of him is often the one in distress. He is the child who may go overboard in seeking escape from his feelings of tension and pressure in the warm feeling of comfort that his body can afford him.

It is high time, I think, that we face the realities of the strong inner sex needs of all people, no matter how young or old. It is high time that we overcome the feeling that sex is dirty, bad, or criminal. *It is not sex itself, but the misuse of it in relation to others, that can be bad.*

Masturbation in moderation is normal. Psychiatrists point out, as a matter of fact, that it would be abnormal if children did not masturbate. Most psychiatrists feel that the short spurts of sexual activity in early childhood and the longer spurt that begins in adolescence actually lay the groundwork for the pathways of feelings needed later for entrance into a full adult sexual relationship.

Natural Needs of the Once-Married

The preceding explanation has relevance to the question of release of sexual tension for the divorced or widowed. How can a person once married, but no longer so, fail to experience sexual tensions? They are inevitable, I believe. The individual may refuse to admit them to himself, but they are there nonetheless. If the first marriage was sound sexually, the person now alone desires sexual activity like that of the past. If the first marriage was sexually unsound, the individual remains in search of a yet unexperienced but still desired ideal.

What to do?

The worst thing would be to seek out someone of the opposite sex—anyone—and delude yourself into thinking that you are in love. Just as foolhardy, of course, is to have a promiscuous relationship for the sheer sake of sexual satisfaction. In both instances the short-term benefits, if any, decrease the chances of a long-term relationship built on true affection. Ideally, you should seek this latter type of sustained relationship that will bring new happiness and new unity to your life. However, it may be a long time in arriving.

I must ask, then, what is so terrible, or so sinful about temporary self-release from sexual tension? I will concede self-release as harmful to the personality only when, at any age, it is used as a substitute for a full and active life, or as a retreat from the responsibilities and challenges that belong to that period of life.

Of course, sexual feelings can be submerged and repressed a great deal of the time. If they could not be, the world would be far more chaotic than it already is. Each of us must learn to live with self-control. Each of us must accept the need for some frustration in all phases of our lives. However, for some divorced or widowed persons, there may come a point when sexual desires become extremely strong and extremely difficult to contain. Far better to have self-release than to indulge in a temporary and therefore shabby relationship. As I have stated, the final goal must always be a new and lasting relationship with a mate of your considered choice.

The formerly married individual with normal sexual desires is faced with but a small number of alternatives: He has temporary affairs, or he indulges in promiscuity, or he abstains completely, or he seeks a new partner maturely. If the quest is long and unrewarding, he may practice self-release. From the standpoints both of his emotional well-being and his social adjustments, I submit that the latter, self-release, fulfills a necessary function.

I expect a great hue and cry to go up objecting to this statement. I suspect that most of the objections will be largely emotionally based. We allow our emotions to overwhelm our intellects in considerations of sex. We fail to approach many aspects of sexual tension, sexual adjustment and sexual manners rationally. As a result, there are untold conflicts between what we know intellectually to be reasonable about sex and what society sanctions.

Perhaps this is most true in the case of the individual who has been divorced or widowed. For as I have said, he has two faces. And the one seen by him alone, albeit dimly at times, can be extremely distressing.

To lessen the distress, the individual must be honest with himself. He should recognize that his needs and desires are not abnormal, but are part of the everyday behavior of human beings everywhere. He must recognize, too, that sexual needs are inevitable. He must be able to choose maturely a method for meeting those sexual needs, and to accept his choice of method in mature fashion.

In other words, if he takes the route toward sham or promiscuity, he must be prepared to endure the consequences. He must recognize sham and promiscuity for what they are. This requires honest appraisal.

Honesty with self is an absolute necessity for the person who is alone. The more honest you can be with yourself, the more you will be able to accept your aloneness.

If you do, your choice of a new mate is likely to reflect sound judgment, rather than satisfaction of a wild need to find the arms of someone—anyone.

15

Love Can Be Ageless

"Both had serene expressions on their faces and they looked continuously from one to the other as if in constant need of reassurance that the miracle of being together after so many years was indeed still real. They seemed to have grown old in the right way, they and their spirits being contained within their age as naturally as a nut is enclosed within its shell, and only when fully ripened falling obediently to the need for a renewal of life. . . ."

These words were written by Laurens Van der Post. They describe a very old Bushman couple he observed on his safari into the Kalahari Desert of Africa. They are good words to be read and remembered by any person who is becoming anxious about the effect his or her age may have on his ability to love.

In the past, it was quite common to consider a woman finished, through, at the age of forty. This was thought to be a magic milestone—black magic—marking the end of enjoyable living to the woman herself, for every woman dreaded reaching this age and the dread was usually passed along to her daughter.

The fears and anxieties surrounding the menopause age make women do strange things. Some dress in clothes designed for teen-agers, to conceal their years. Others dye their hair; others increase the use of make-up. Still others change their patterns of behavior in order to imitate younger persons. Some women do all these things at once—so that meeting such a one can be a nightmarish experience.

Fortunately, most women have discovered dread of the menopause to be quite needless, and that the thing they had been taught to fear really is not fearful.

What Is Menopause?

Like other words that conjure anxieties and tensions, menopause is little understood. The simplest explanation is this: It is the period of a woman's life when she ceases to be fertile. Why then should this be feared? You would expect that most women of forty-five to fifty-five (the menopause years, as a rule) would welcome such a change. It is the rare woman indeed who seeks to become pregnant after the age of forty-five. As a matter of fact, I doubt that any such exist—at least not if they are thinking clearly.

Why does the idea of menopause frighten us so, then? Because we have surrounded the idea of the cessation of fertility with a great many wrong concepts. One of them is that the menopause in women spells the end of all pleasurable sexual activity. This is sheer nonsense, of course, as countless husbands and wives know. Another idea associated with menopause is that during this phase of life, a woman's mental capabilities decrease, or are somehow impaired. Nothing could be further from the truth.

These are but two of the incorrect beliefs surrounding the menopause. There are others: that some women go insane; that women turn ugly; that men inevitably find menopausal women distasteful; that menopause is a major cause of divorce. All of these are pure fiction.

The basic facts too often have been submerged. The menopause is a normal part of living. The end of ovulation has nothing to do with a woman's mental or sexual powers or her mental health. The unrealistic attitudes in people's minds about the menopause would be silly if they did not so often lead to extreme unhappiness.

Menopause and Pregnancy

No one knows exactly when during menopause the ovary actually stops producing ova. Late pregnancies even up to the age of fifty have been known. Some of these have been said to occur even after menstruation apparently had ceased. Like many other aspects of sex and human reproduction, this area has not been very well studied or understood.

At the beginning of menstruation, around the age of twelve or thirteen, there may be a period of several months or even a year or two when the girl menstruates regularly, but does not yet produce an ovum. The same thing may happen toward the end of a woman's reproductive period, but not necessarily.

Therefore when a woman asks advice as to how soon after the menopause she may consider herself to be safe from pregnancy, she should be told to continue whatever birth control methods previously were used effectively for at least two years after the last menstrual period. So much for the problem of the woman's fertility. Now what about the other changes that occur at the same period?

The Process of Menopause

It is important both for men and women to understand that in the menopause, along with cessation of ovulation, other changes in the ovary occur. Until this period the ovary has produced, in regular cycles, two distinct sex hormones.

The first is estrogen, which is produced during the entire reproductive life of a woman. Its production is regulated by the pituitary gland, a small, oval "master switch" located at the base of the brain. The pituitary is, indeed, the regulating factor of all the glands in the body that produce hormones.

A second hormone is produced in the ovary, this, however, only in connection with ovulation. Each month, after the ovum is released from the ovary, certain cells in the little group of cells that surrounded the ovum begin to change, to multiply, and to produce a hormone called progesterone.

These cells form what is called the "corpus luteum," and the progesterone made by it is apparently there in case of pregnancy. If the ovum is not fertilized, and passes out of the body —in other words, if no pregnancy occurs—progesterone production by the corpus luteum cells stops suddenly, and when the progesterone level in the blood drops, menstruation begins.

If, however, the ovum has been fertilized and implants itself in the uterus, a message apparently is carried from the uterus via the pituitary to the corpus luteum, because the latter continues to produce progesterone throughout the nine months of the pregnancy. The hormones I have been discussing are truly remarkable. Most often, a single drop the size of the head of a pin or even less, is all that is needed by the body to carry out one or another vital function.

At the menopause when ovulation stops occurring, there is no more progesterone being produced, for there is no corpus luteum to produce it. Thereafter, this hormone is missing from the picture. At the same time, the production of estrogen from the other cells of the ovary, which has been proceeding more or less steadily ever since puberty, begins gradually to diminish.

It is this decrease of estrogen level in the body which may produce some of the admittedly uncomfortable symptoms of the menopause, such as hot flushes, dizziness and palpitation. Unquestionably these symptoms can range from mild to fairly severe.

Treatment for Symptoms of Menopause

There is no reason why physical symptoms of menopause should cause undue and prolonged discomfort. There is no reason why any woman should suffer such symptoms and feel cursed by "change of life," a term which seems silly and unnecessary.

If symptoms are caused by a too-sudden lowering of the estrogen level of the body, then the simplest thing to do is to provide some extra estrogen to bolster this level while the body is accustoming itself to the lower level. This is exactly what physicians do today, usually with excellent results.

Emotions and the Menopause

Of course, there are other symptoms associated with the menopause. Emotional depression sometimes accompanies it. It is extremely difficult at times to distinguish between which symptoms are primarily emotional and which are primarily physical. However, both are closely intertwined.

Let no one think that emotional symptoms are not based on real causes. The old days of saying, "You're just imagining all this," are gone. Symptoms of menopause certainly are not imaginary. These normal changes in your body may very well play a great part in the kind of symptoms you have.

If you have been the type of high-strung woman who takes everything intensely and personally so that *any* discomfort seems almost a personal insult, if you feel "this should not happen to me," the chances are you will be emotionally distressed by a multitude of normal life situations, including a perfectly normal menopause. When you take something hard, when you are overconcerned about it, or resentful of it, this alone can increase the severity of symptoms.

Even such women, nowadays, can be helped over the emotional rough spots of the menopause. A comparatively new family of drugs called "psychic energizers" often can pull women up out of their depressions. Successful case histories are piling up to the credit of these drugs. One woman who went into an emotional tailspin for a full year was helped greatly to return to normal by them.

Still other drugs can be used to ease specific symptoms such as dizziness, quickened heart rate, flushes and any upset in elimination.

Three Ways to Tension Release

Recently, a distinguished obstetrician from the University of Maryland, Dr. John C. Dumler, was conducting a seminar at a medical meeting. He discussed the problems of menopause for about a half-hour and then presented his notions as to how menopause can be made easier for most women. I agree with his conclusions and I offer them to you here as valuable thoughts.

First, the woman should be educated (preferably by her physician) as to exactly what takes place in menopause. Second, the husband should also be educated so that he can cooperate fully in easing the tensions in this life stage. Thus, it is advisable for the husband to accompany his wife to the physician when the first signs of menopause appear. In this way, the husband can be made sensitive to the needs and feelings of his wife.

The first two steps will go far toward lessening the effects of menopause, both physical and emotional. Finally, the third step is this: persistent symptoms should be recognized by the woman, discussed with her physician, and some treatment instituted *if* the physician deems it necessary. However, if steps one and two are followed through, there will be less need for step three and correspondingly less need for medication.

The Menopause As a Weapon

Earlier, I discussed how men and women use sex as a weapon or a reward. The menopause also can be used as a weapon. Some women who never have been able to achieve a really satisfactory sexual relationship, or who have been battling through life with men to prove how superior but how ill-used women are, find menopause a welcome event. They clutch at the notion that menopause is the end of everything, including sex. Thus, without any guilty conscience whatever, they can take a deep breath and sigh with relief that they no longer have to worry about "that" any more.

The husbands of these women then find themselves completely denied any sexual relationship whatsoever. Frequently, this does not represent a radical change from the past, inasmuch as the sexual relationship in their marriage has not been deep and warm at any time. It is a sad thing to think of such marriages. It is sad, too, to contemplate the use to which a normal menopause is put by such ill-adjusted women. The tragedy is intensified when you consider that the menopause and beyond can and does represent periods of peak sexual satisfaction for many couples. I would like to stress this.

Sex in Menopause and Beyond

As I stated previously, the production of estrogen does not cease. It simply diminishes. A sexual life which has been warm and full until the menopause will certainly continue to be warm and full. In addition, there are other positive aspects vital to release from sexual tensions.

The woman in menopause or beyond is completely free of all inhibitory activities that have to do with the monthly period and concern about pregnancy. How many women have said to me, "I started enjoying sex for the first time after I was forty-five!"

For the first time in their married lives, husband and wife can make love if, as, when and how they want. The old requirements no longer apply. They can indulge any caprice or whim. They can select any time or place. They can toss away old rules about frequency of intercourse. This total release can be a heady one which produces glowing results for both partners.

I know of many couples in middle life who have discovered their new sexual freedom and feel truly liberated. One in particular has told me of their experience. In twenty years of marriage the wife had rather restrained herself. The couple had had two children and though, of course, they continued to have intercourse, it was infrequent. Suddenly, both husband and wife heaved almost audible sighs of relief when she experienced the first symptoms of the menopause. "Finally," the husband said, "you will be able to consider sex as something other than a threat of pregnancy." She did and they are both happier for it.

This case highlights still another important point. Far too many people consider sex the exclusive prerogative of youth. Along with this baseless notion goes another—that sex in the mature, middle-aged individual is not quite decent. This is one of the great inconsistencies in our cultural thinking. It is inconsistent to glorify youth and urge that a fifty-year-old woman dress and behave like a young girl (as our culture does) while on the other hand condemning her for making an attempt to live youthfully. To a great many people, it is quite discomforting to think that a woman of fifty could ever lose her cool, calm, well-manicured, well-coifed, collected air and enjoy going to bed with her husband. Yet why shouldn't she?

The Fears Women Have

President Franklin D. Roosevelt once said in a memorable speech following his first inauguration—when the banks were closed and panic was in the air—"The only thing we have to fear is fear itself." Medically this is a most sound observation.

Not long ago, I was called upon by a large group of women to speak about menopause. When I arrived at the meeting the ladies had just finished luncheon. I walked in expecting to find that most of them would be in their forties or beyond. What did I see? About two hundred women, none of whom, with very few exceptions, could have been a day over thirty-five. I was quite taken aback, because it seemed to me that I could not appropriately offer them the material that I had prepared.

After a few halting introductory sentences, I stopped, peered at them and asked, "How many of you are grandmothers?" Three hands went into the air. Then I burst out, "Will you, for heaven's sake, explain to me why you invited me here to talk about the menopause? Almost none of you is anywhere near that time." A babble of voices started to answer. I made out from all sides the words: "We thought you could help us prepare for it."

This really shook me. Why under the sun should women of thirty-five and under need to be "prepared" for the menopause, that is unless they were scared to death of it? Obviously, they were. I spent the next hour saying to them more or less what I have written in this chapter and I scolded them for being such worry-warts. I told them that after hate, fear and anxiety are the worst enemies of any of the bodily processes; that if they approached their menopausal years filled with fear and anxiety, the chances of their having trouble during those years would be increased. Further, I said that if they forgot about menopause until they were well past it and concentrated all their efforts on living and loving, they would be far better off.

I told them then and I repeat now: If you do concentrate all your effort on living a full life, I don't see any reason why 99 percent of you shouldn't sail through the menopause hardly realizing that you have done so.

Sex in the Later Years

The inevitable question as to whether sex life stops with menopause came up at the meeting I have just mentioned. I told the audience the story of a woman friend who assured me that her sexual relationship with her husband, which had always been good, not only continued so, but became increasingly better until they were both well into their seventies.

When I finished this story, there were titters in the audience.

Then I told about the woman I knew who had been married to two men in her lifetime. With each of them, she had failed to achieve sexual satisfaction. Her second husband died when she was fifty-five. At the age of seventy, she fell in love with and married a man of her own age. With him, *for the first time in her life,* she experienced full sexual satisfaction. Once again titters arose from the assemblage.

This gave me an added opportunity to ask these women quite forcefully what was so funny about successful sex, or any sex for that matter, in a woman of seventy? Of course, I received no satisfactory reply, for they had none. No, sexual fulfillment is not the private preserve of the young. Indeed, it should not be.

What an opportunity we miss if we cut off, by our attitudes and beliefs, all possibility of continued sexual fulfillment beyond the age of fifty. Our children grow up and venture forth into the world. What remains? Marriage, husband and wife, the greatest of all relationships, the relationship between a man and woman who are more important to each other than anyone else in the world, even the children they have borne and reared.

How lucky that man and that woman if, in that wonderful combination of long-time union and new-found freedom, they feel free to continue to express physically that deep communion which is theirs, which belongs uniquely to them and to them alone.

The Male Climacteric

Thus far, I have mentioned nothing about the male and changes in his sexual capacities as he ages. Much has been written and said in recent years about the male climacteric. Does anyone really know much about it? I doubt it.

In this area as in others, the kind of person you have been may well determine what happens to you at this time. If you have been a hypochondriac-type of male, given to fears and worries about yourself, the so-called male climacteric may be more difficult for you than it need be.

Male Symptoms

Generally, the male climacteric comes later than that of the female. Men may experience fatigue, headache, jitteriness, stomach pain and other symptoms between ages fifty and sixty. For the male hypochondriac, the first symptom of fatigue means to him a waning of his sexual prowess. This is hardly the fact.

However, as soon as symptoms appear, if you allow your tensions to increase, sexual appetite and capability will almost certainly decrease. Then, of course, you may find yourself with some mild potency problems. These interactions of tension and decreased sexual capacity may continue and ultimately lead to more serious potency disturbances.

Therapy for the Male

Symptoms of climacteric, if pronounced, should be reported to the physician. As with the female, hormone therapy has proved beneficial in a great many cases, in this instance, of course, male hormone rather than female hormone being replaced.

In addition to hormone therapy, there are a good many tried and tested drugs which control stomach symptoms, head pain, lassitude and associated disorders. As a matter of fact, many eminent authorities in the field have been moved to say that almost no male need be troubled by symptoms of climacteric, what with present-day medications and knowledge.

Does the Male Lose His "Sex"?

Of course, age brings with it a decreased sexual capacity for many men. However, "decreased sexual activity" does not mean that the individual need completely lose his sexual desires or capability. Many men continue an active sex life until they are sixty, seventy and over.

The vigorous male who lives hard and fully, and has learned to love equally hard and fully, stands the best chance of retaining sexual capability. This type of male, who has achieved a permanent relationship in which he finds and gives satisfaction, and in which he feels secure, can weather all types of ups and downs, including some normal reduction in his sexual activities. For him, there will be little discomfort, physical or emotional, in the male climacteric. He will forge ahead through the so-called climacteric years without considering them a danger period at all.

There is a thought with which I would like to leave you, whether you are a man or a woman. Difficulties of the middle years have been intensified by misinformation and by myth. As a result, needless fears have grown up concerning the "trials" of the forties, fifties and beyond. Facts can dissolve these fears.

For at the root of most emotional disturbances, no matter what their form or expression, lies fear—and most fear is needless, being based on lack of knowledge.

16

The Ebb and Flow of Sexual Desire

When they are married, most young couples assume that their sexual desires as to frequency, time, place and method will somehow coincide. How naïve! This is like saying that every day the weather is completely predictable.

In each individual there is an ebb and flow of sexual desire and need created by conditioning and circumstance. It will help young couples, and older ones too, if they understand that cycles of need as regards sexuality are perfectly normal. They are a part of virtually every marriage.

At the outset of marriage, we have two people, comparative strangers to each other's intimate and innermost thoughts and needs. As I have said, the first few years of marriage represent a period of discovery, and one of the most vital discoveries is that concerning the differences in sexual appetite. That is why it is so important to communicate freely and to be patient with each other. It may take five, ten, even twenty years for near-perfect accord to be reached in the area of physical love—if it ever is reached.

In the simplest terms, the ebb and flow of sexual desire can be explained this way: Husband or wife at any given moment may want intercourse or some form of sex play; the other not. Here are the seeds of conflict, or at least of disagreement. If disagreement and carping become a fixed pattern in sex life, disaster can result.

The ways in which these differences in sex need can express themselves are endless. I know a woman who goes on what can be called "sex jags." For no apparent reason, once every two or three months, her sexual appetite increases to such a pitch that she desires intercourse five, six, seven times in twenty-four hours.

Then, there's the case of the fifty-five-year-old prosperous businessman. His wife reports that, since the age of fifty, he has insisted that they have intercourse every night, because he thinks he might be losing his sexual prowess and must prove to himself that he is "still the man he once was."

I know a twenty-nine-year-old mother who is "very social." She seems to live for parties and gay moments. She will never have intercourse with her husband on the night before a big social event, because she believes that this will make her too tired, too "washed out" to act her best at the party.

These cases will give you an idea of the broad range of reasons for cycles in sexual appetite. Of course, there are probably thousands of other reasons, some of which can be explained and others which cannot.

Career versus Sex Needs

Occupational and related economic factors are important to sexual urges or lack of them. Stress in the job can produce a feeling of temporary disinterest in sex for the husband or wife. Particular job problems that come once a year or once every six months can do this, too. Sweating out a raise, a promotion, or a big contract can so preoccupy one partner or the other that he becomes less sexually active.

Couples must understand these occupational factors and adjust to them. There are no arbitrary rules for frequency of sexual intercourse. Couples should understand this even though they normally prefer to have it once a week, twice, five or even ten times. If there is some kind of occupational stress, the normal pattern for them can be temporarily disrupted.

At times, occupational factors can produce different reactions in terms of sexual desires on the part of different individuals. I know two young writers. One, when working on a difficult assignment with deadline and editor breathing down his neck, has an almost unlimited capacity for sex. He and his wife are likely to have intercourse three times or more a day during the "pressure of work" period.

The second writer is just the opposite. He becomes so engrossed in the assignment that little else seems to matter, including sex. When he is "on deadline" he will not go to bed with his wife. He is too preoccupied, too abstracted or both. Both couples have learned how to adjust to these variations.

The Household Itself As a Sex Regulator

Just as a husband's sexual urges may be enhanced or decreased by career factors, so a wife's may be affected by household factors. Caring for children, housework, financial worries—these and a host of other "home factors" can be at the root of sexual desires or lack of them.

I know a young New Jersey housewife who became so preoccupied with the purchase of a new home and all its accompanying problems that she refused to have intercourse with her husband for almost a month. Uppermost in her mind were worries about getting a bank loan so they could obtain the new house. For three weeks the loan was uncertain. During this period, the wife worried herself into a near frenzy and was totally unresponsive to her husband's advances. When the loan came through, she immediately resumed their normal sexual relations with renewed intensity.

Influence of Outside Forces on Physical Love

The list is almost endless of outside forces that can influence the sexual participation of husband and wife. In-law problems certainly can be one factor, parents another. A friend of mine becomes sexually neutral every time she has a raging argument with her mother. Another young woman I know shies away from intercourse with her husband when their parents are visiting. This probably stems from fear of being overheard.

It is obvious that the factors involved in the variations in sexual appetite are virtually endless. Each partner in a marriage should learn to expect them and to live with them. By so doing, they will greatly decrease sexual tensions.

Smoothing Out the Sex Cycles

One way to smooth the peaks and troughs of sex desire is to make an earnest effort to retain spontaneity in physical love.

How many women have told me that sex for them has degenerated into a predictable routine which follows automatically every time the husband does some characteristic thing that has always signaled his desire for sex. At least, this is the belief of those wives to whom sex has become humdrum and uninteresting.

To maintain sexual interest at a comparatively high pitch, it is necessary to keep sex spontaneous. One couple's experience may apply to others. Every three months or so, this couple hires a nurse for their children and goes away for the week end. Completely free of obligations, they can be carefree in every way, including sex. And they are.

Still others have found that spontaneity in sex can be achieved through following normal love impulses. Intensifying pre-coitus play is one route. One wife told me that her husband "just wanted intercourse" and none of the preliminaries. When she explained to him that this displeased her, they experimented with various ways to increase love play leading to the final act, with resulting satisfaction for both. Expressions of love on the beach, in cars, in speech over a restaurant table—all are good in providing a climate of affection that is so necessary for successful physical love.

It should be remembered that the surest way to receive love and affection is to offer them first.

When the Male Is "Frigid"

We have already explored the subject of the so-called frigid wife. However, little has been written or said about the "frigid" male, or the male who seemingly is passive when it comes to the subject of physical love.

It is assumed by most people that the husband is more eager than his wife in matters sexual. While this often is the case, it is not inevitable. As a matter of fact, more and more instances are coming to light in which the problem in a particular marriage is the somewhat passive male.

Some men, of course, like some women, are naturally rather docile and retiring. These men appear to have decreased sex drives. Their restraint in other aspects of living spills over to the area of sexuality. Like their female counterparts, they are rarely truly frigid, nor do they necessarily have homosexual tendencies. They simply may be less capable of being sexually aroused than their wives. This is not necessarily a sign of weakness. It is certainly not an indicator of impotence.

Woman's Need for Reassurance

Sometimes for the wife who desires intercourse more often than her husband, other factors may be at work. To understand these, the husband must realize that, to a sensitive woman, sex means a great deal more than the act itself. Actually, it is a symbol, a kind of shorthand expression of all the things the woman feels about the man to whom she has joined her life.

It is almost impossible for most men to understand this because most men can enjoy sex quite outside of love. However, to a woman who feels deeply about her husband, it is almost a physical impossibility for her to enjoy the sex act without love. Therefore, the sex act for her symbolizes the love that she hopes, wishes, longs for, and expects, from her husband.

Now, if there is any doubt in her mind as to her husband's love for her she will begin to act out of a need for reassurance. She will challenge her husband more and more frequently with sexual demands, if only to demonstrate to herself that he does, indeed, love her.

The original doubt, or seed of doubt, in the wife's mind may not derive from any profound cause or anything as striking as infidelity, but may spring from some quite ordinary thing. The husband's overattention to outside activities, such as work, is a common cause.

In this regard, what seem to men to be small details of life are often deeply important to women. The overlooking of such details can cause a wife to doubt her husband's love. The man who forgets a birthday or anniversary has long been the butt of jokes and cartoons. However, to a wife, forgetting such an occasion is no laughing matter. There can be a terrible feeling of loneliness in the woman who, while constantly making gestures of thoughtfulness to her husband and family, hardly ever receives such gestures in return.

The reassurance such a woman gets from small gestures, a telephone call, a postcard, an inexpensive gift out of season—this reassurance can establish the climate for a happier adjustment in marital sex. Perhaps this and only this is what might be needed in most cases.

Remember, by the very nature of a woman's life, she commits her heart in every home activity. If she does not receive from her husband a demonstration that his heart is just as deeply involved, she may grow unsure of the worth of her own commitment.

Adjusting to Each Other's Sexual Needs

Recently a young husband wrote me saying: "We are particularly interested in solving a problem regarding the frequency of sexual relations." In this instance, it appeared that the wife's needs exceeded those of her husband.

I replied to that man, pointing out that of course sex is a symbol of the deepest importance to people, and that sex is used in many ways by many individuals. Following is an excerpt from my letter to him:

"We are brought up not to talk about our sexual needs, hardly even to think about them, although most of us have periods of obsession with them at one time or another. Depending on our upbringing, our efforts to subjugate our sexual impulses before marriage, and our reactions to the sense of guilt about sex that our culture almost inevitably imposes, one of two things takes place. Either there is a strengthening of sexual drive or a weakening of it, to the point that when release in marriage is achieved, we may find ourselves with a solution of our own problems not in the same key as the solution our sexual partner has arrived at by a different route.

"This may be what has happened in the case of you and your wife. You therefore would need to answer quite a few questions for yourselves. For instance, what has made each of you arrive at your present situation, what conflicts are being resolved by an increased drive in your wife's case or a decreased drive in your own case? As a matter of fact, what do you mean by 'increased' and 'decreased'? We know that entirely normal frequency of intercourse for couples varies all the way from several times a day to several times a month. It appears that in the case of any one couple, the drive of one partner can be considered excessive only with relation to the drive of the other partner and not with relation to any established norm, which, I repeat, is nonexistent.

"The case where the wife's desire is greater than the husband's is more difficult of solution than the converse. It is obvious that when the husband desires intercourse more frequently than the wife, a truly loving wife can easily gratify the husband's desire without necessarily feeling that she must achieve orgasm. The converse is not true, simply because the husband cannot always achieve erection unless he feels desire.

"There are other ways, however, of resolving the situation. First of all, the wife can explore carefully the background of why she has what seems to her husband greater desire than his.

She may find that, as she explores, her desires become somewhat modified because she may discover that she is using this desire to prove something, to win a point or for some other reason.

"The husband may, out of his love and desire for happiness of the wife, re-examine his own background carefully and honestly. He may find that it is perhaps a puritanical or repressed upbringing that is preventing him from feeling free to enjoy sexual intercourse as often as his wife. In any case, he might also, by caresses, both manual and oral, gratify his wife's desire on occasions when he himself feels none. . . ."

As I have said, there are a good many cases in which the problem expresses itself the other way around, that is where the husband's sexual demands exceed the desires of his wife. Following is a letter I received stating this aspect of the problem, along with excerpts of my reply:

"I am married and have a problem in sexual relations with my husband. I think it might break us up or make our marriage unhappy. We have been married four years and my husband still feels that every night we should have intercourse. When I try to talk to him about giving me a chance to want him, he tells me that would be too long a wait.

"I'm beginning to feel it's my duty and the enjoyment is decreasing every day. I have never really learned to enjoy it. . . . Recently, he's started telling me how other women do things to let the man know they're enjoying it. We have three kids and our marriage must be saved. Please tell me what to do."

To this distraught wife and mother, I replied:

"One of the most difficult things in marriage is to adjust the sexual desires of the two people involved. There is no such thing as 'too much' or 'too little' because each person feels differently at different times. It will help if your husband understands that most of the time, a woman is slower to develop her desire than a man. You might therefore work out the following kind of compromise:

"If your husband desires intercourse every night, why not? There is no reason why you and he should feel that you *must* respond to him every single time. There is no reason why, when you do not feel particularly responsive, that you should not indicate this to him, but at the same time indicate your pleasure at giving him pleasure. Thus, he would have intercourse with you knowing that although you might not be achieving orgasm, he would be free to enjoy his contact with you completely.

"On the other hand, whenever you indicated the need for it, he could show great consideration and love for you by prolonging the preliminary love-making, perhaps as much as half an hour or an hour, at least until you indicated whether or not you were aroused. A woman generally can tell whether she is going to be aroused sufficiently to achieve orgasm. If after a sufficient time has elapsed you feel you are not going to have orgasm, you can indicate this to him and he can proceed at his own pace.

"There is no reason for a woman to have orgasm every time. Furthermore, your husband should realize that you are in the age range where sexual desire is somewhat less high. Contrary to the man, who has his sexual peak in the early twenties, there is lower sexual desire in the woman at this age. She is likely to reach her peak in the late thirties or early forties and then continue at quite a high level, sexually, through menopause and into the sixties.

"Both you and your husband need to remember, too, that you, the wife, must not only take care of the children, but of the home as well. This is the difference between you and the 'other women' your husband has mentioned. Whatever his knowledge of them, it was on a sexual basis only and not on a husband-and-wife basis. Over a period of years, the husband-and-wife relationship becomes far deeper and contains far greater satisfactions than mere transitory sexual activity. . . ."

What such couples need to do is what I have offered previously as a key to release from sexual anxieties. Re-edit the film of your life's experiences. Do away with those concepts that you find destructive. Substitute productive ideas and desires, all the while keeping yourself flexible and suggestible.

Remember that the ebb and flow of sexual desire is normal, but that differences between husband and wife can be lessened only if each makes an honest effort for the sake of the other.

17

Religion and Sexual Tensions

If there is any area in which sex has no business being a problem, that one area is religion. The very idea that the way one person loves God and worships Him could ever be a means of separating that person from a beloved one is a contradiction in itself. But this does happen in spite of all our good will and intentions, and it happens, I believe, mainly because human beings have two unfortunate tendencies. One is to care more about the details and dogma of a religious belief than about the fundamental part of that belief, namely the love and worship of God; the other is, in moments of stress, to use the nearest and most hurtful weapon possible against the other fellow, and very often that weapon is the other fellow's religion.

BEFORE MARRIAGE

Prevention of Religious Conflict

Here, if anywhere, is one area subject to good preventive action, and that is open, frank discussion and decision-making *before marriage* between partners who do not share the same religious faith. Most people shy away from this. They are afraid of "hurting" or "offending" the other person, forgetting that after marriage, unsolved religious problems may well cause one partner deliberately to hurt or offend the other, once the newness of marriage has worn off. It is much better to find out what areas of agreement can be reached regarding certain knotty problems prior to marriage itself. If agreement cannot be reached and *written down* ahead of the marriage, then at least the partners should know that they are going into marriage with one type of conflict already at work in the marriage.

Religious Areas to Explore

Before marriage, then, what are some of the areas of difference between major religious faiths that should be explored, and explored thoroughly? I would say the most important are, for Jews, the keeping of dietary laws and observance of the Sabbath; for Catholics, attendance at Mass and the Sacraments, birth control, observance of fasts, and legal abortion on medical grounds. With Protestants, the situation is a little different, inasmuch as most of the denominations are permissive and exhortative rather than mandatory in their requirements. Some of the more fundamentalist sects, however, have almost as strict rules as the Catholic and Jewish religions and, of course, such groups as the Latter Day Saints and the Amish and Mennonites are unique in their requirements and extremely strict. For all groups one great basic question is what faith the children are to be brought up in.

Many people are quite glib in the promises they give before marriage because they have not thought them through ahead of time. Because marriage occurs at a very young age in most cases, it happens that the marriage coincides with the very age when many young people take their religion less seriously than they may later. This may trap the young engaged persons into brushing aside as unimportant some requirement of their religion that they may later revert to feeling is absolutely essential. This is why it is so important to talk out ahead of time all of the religious aspects of the forthcoming marriage.

True Religious Understanding

I do not think this is the place to discuss the details of the attitudes of the various religions on the specific questions I noted above, and I would be presumptuous if I tried to do so. Most of us say that we respect the next man's religious convictions, but this is usually only until we run up against one that differs from ours. Each engaged partner, therefore, should make very sure of his understanding of the attitude of his own religion on all questions. Then he must make very sure that he understands the attitudes of his partner's religion on the same questions. The two people about to be married should then talk these over carefully, because if there is no meeting of minds at this time, then later on there is likely to be a separation of hearts, and a hurtful one at that.

On the subject of bringing up the children, it can be very easy for the one partner who feels less strongly about his religion to agree to have the children brought up in the other one's faith. Five or ten years later the first partner may suddenly become aware that his children are being taught something which he violently disbelieves. For instance, the attitude of Protestants on the subject of masturbation is entirely different from the attitude of Catholics. It is essential that these attitudes be thoroughly explored by both partners, with the religious counselors of both partners. Talking things out ahead of time never hurt anyone, and may prevent a great deal of subsequent sorrow and difficulty.

AFTER MARRIAGE

Sex and Mixed Marriage

Often the question is asked, "Can a mixed marriage be jeopardized by the differing attitudes on sex of the two partners' religious beliefs?" Yes, it can, even if the couple is genuinely in love, and especially if they have not learned to communicate freely with each other. Each of the religious groups tends to look quite pessimistically on the outcome of such a marriage, because they are realistic in facing the fact that a religiously mixed marriage has certain handicaps. This does not mean, however, that many mixed marriages have not turned out wonderfully in every respect.

Most important to the total marriage, sex included, is not the question of one or another religious affiliation but rather that of the couple's desire to express love, to grow in marriage, and really to learn to know and appreciate each other. Certainly, differing religious beliefs may give husband and wife differing orientations for sex. However, the critical question is not, does a mixed marriage jeopardize sex? Rather, it is, does a mixed marriage prevent each partner from accepting himself and his mate fully in all aspects? If the partners are truly mature and are making a conscious effort toward the goal of mutual acceptance, the answer should be, "No!"

Greater unity in mixed marriages can come about if both partners remain open-minded in the matter of the other mate's way of worshiping. The greatest good can come of occasional participation in the partner's religious services in order that each may experience the unifying realization that the presence of God is the same in church, temple, or meeting-house. A human being should not be so narrow in his convictions as to allow the details of ritual and worship to come between him and God.

You may ask, if a couple is aware that mixed marriage may impose some problems, why do they attempt it in the first place? Some couples are so attracted to each other for a variety of reasons that religious difference may take a back seat, at least temporarily.

However, some mixed marriages are clearly the result of one or the other partner's desire to rebel against parental authority or some other form of authority. This is a major factor, I believe, in mixed marriages as well as in other marriages. The young person feels, consciously or unconsciously, that he must throw off the bonds of parental control. In his rebellion, he chooses to hurl a real stone of defiance by marrying someone outside his religion. This may equally motivate him to marry someone outside his social group, outside his race, or outside his age range.

The critical question which must be asked by those who are so motivated is this: Is the need to defy authority greater than the love I feel for my prospective marriage partner? If the answer is yes, the marriage may flounder. If the answer is no, it has a far better chance of succeeding. To arrive at an honest answer one way or the other may require the help of an expert.

I know a couple whose experience illustrates this last point nicely. The wife is Jewish and the husband is a Methodist. They have been married for a good many years and their marriage has had its share of problems, some of them arising from the fact that they are of different religious backgrounds.

A few years ago, the wife decided to find out once and for all if she was motivated to marry a non-Jew because of her need to defy her parents. (She readily admitted that this was part of the picture.) She spent considerable time with a marriage counselor who had good training in psychology.

At the end of many sessions, the wife and the counselor concluded that she did need to throw off parental control and the need was strong indeed. However, they also concluded that she would have married her husband under any circumstances. She did, after all, love him very deeply, despite their differences. Since the wife discovered her true feelings—and she did a great deal with her own film memory record—she and her husband have been far happier and easier about their different beliefs.

The Role of Religious Counselors

Clergymen of all faiths have begun to realize that their training as clergymen has not automatically turned them into perfect men without problems, any more than medical training turns physicians into perfect men. There is nothing magic about being a clergyman or a doctor. Each is a human being first, with the same difficulties, weaknesses and problems as any other human beings, and only secondly is he a professional. Both come into contact with the most sensitive areas in a person's life, the clergyman with his parishioner's religious life, and the physician with his patient's sex life. These two lives, of course, are never completely separate.

Until recently, however, little training was given in either profession in dealing constructively with the most intimate problems of troubled human beings. As a matter of fact, little has been done to help the minister or the doctor solve his own personal problem. We all know the old saying, "Physician, heal thyself." This is never more true than with relation to religion and to sex.

In the past few years the clergy has taken steps to improve the situation. Various religious groups have made significant strides in establishing training courses for religious leaders in what is called "Pastoral Counseling." The Roman Catholic Church, through its Pre-Cana and Cana Conferences with engaged and married couples, carries on an intensive effort to orient young people to the variety of problems encountered in marriage, and Roman Catholic priests are receiving special training in such counseling. In the same way, in the great religious seminaries, Protestant and Jewish clergymen are taking courses in the Psychology of Marriage and Pastoral Counseling. This means that even if you are removed from family associations and friends there is someone to turn to with your problems—your religious counselor.

In the long run, however, you must do the most important part of adjusting in marriage yourself, by delving deep into your own attitudes and emotions (remember your memory film) to establish the real meaning to you of religion in marriage—and in your whole life.

Religion As a Weapon

If religious differences have become apparent to you in your marriage, then you must take stock to discover whether you are using religion as a club in an attempt to subjugate your partner. It is not a happy thought, but this does take place. And here the basic question is not the difference in religion, but why you need any kind of club in the first place. The purpose of marriage after all is not to win out over your partner. And the main purpose of religion is to express God's love, not your hate.

No matter how different your religious upbringing or how wide apart the religious groups to which you and your partner belong, one common thread of belief runs through all of them: the belief in the one universal God of Christian, Jew and Moslem. All these people believe in the basic principles of living under God and of expressing love for one's fellow man—

preferably beginning with the one nearest and dearest to you.

Selfishness and hostility should have no place in marriage. Least of all should they be allowed to influence our religious feelings or our feelings toward our partners.

That the Kingdom of God is far from being with us now does not relieve us of responsibility to work toward it in our own homes.

18

Who Can Help?

If the question, "Who can help?" had been asked twenty-five years ago, the answer necessarily would have had to limit itself to perhaps not more than three or four kinds of professional people. Nowadays, however, there are many more kinds of people who are qualified to help with marital problems.

Modern medicine recognizes two great divisions: preventive and therapeutic. The preventive part of medical practice is designed to do just what it says—that is, to anticipate medical conditions that might occur in the individual and to take proper means to forestall their occurrence. If actual prevention is not possible, the aim is to make the occurrence of these medical conditions as mild as possible.

Therapeutic medicine, on the other hand, is that division of medical practice that diagnoses and then treats a condition after it has developed, after there are clear-cut symptoms. Theoretically, of course, preventive medicine should be so successful that therapeutic medicine would be unnecessary. This is true in many cases. For instance, diphtheria, which used to be one of the major killing diseases of childhood, is now, because of a simple preventive medical measure, immunization, so rare that medical students may go through their entire four years of medical school without seeing a case. On the other hand, a variety of conditions are still mysterious. For these no therapeutic methods have been developed, much less preventive measures.

In the same way, the modern approach to the ailing marriage has been divided into two phases: prevention and treatment. The preventive phase generally consists of an educational program designed to help young people approach marriage with as much knowledge and understanding as possible. Theoretically, of course, all the things that happen in the young person's life up to the time of marriage might be called education for marriage. The kind of home he was born into is vital; the degree of harmony or lack of harmony; the relationship between his two parents; their ability to communicate to the growing child knowledge and ideals regarding marriage; the kind of people the child met in his life; the kind of courses he had in high school and college—I have shown that these can all be considered a part of the young person's preparation for marriage. Specific courses in education for marriage are provided in many cities, but they are all too few in proportion to the enormously large number of marriages that occur each year. I described some of these courses in an earlier chapter. It is a pity that more of the young people who live where these courses are available do not take advantage of them.

Despite this type of preventive measure, some marriages do

become sick. These marriages then must call for therapeutic help from individuals and services especially geared to provide such help.

Before discussing the kinds of help available, remember that just as it takes two people to make a marriage, so it takes two people to save a marriage. On the other hand, it takes only one person to wreck a marriage.

How You Can Help Your Ailing Marriage

The first person on my list of people who can help will surprise some: it is *you—yourself*. Actually, you are the most important person on the therapeutic team. No marriage can be helped or saved if you yourself are not interested in saving it. And the you-yourself applies to both partners in the marriage.

What can you-yourself do? The first step is to become aware of the need for help. Much stress has been placed on the need for early diagnosis of cancer. This means that we have to be taught when to seek help—as early as possible to avoid serious consequences. The same thing might be said about marriage. I do not mean that you should run to a professional whenever you have a quarrel! Many marriages falter in which quarrels have been conspicuous by their absence, and some quarreling can even strengthen a marriage. No, the signs of an ailing marriage sometimes are almost unobservable to the naked eye. It is the inner eye, the sensitivity and awareness of the partners in the marriage, which must be alert to the earliest symptoms.

Actually, the task of admitting to yourself that something may be wrong with your marriage is one of the most difficult ones human beings are called upon to perform, for this implies that there may be something wrong with you-yourself. Certainly this is difficult for anyone even to contemplate. Something goes wrong with the water pipes in the house and we immediately call in the plumber. We notice one day that the paint on the house has weathered badly and is flaking, but this doesn't shame us so much that we refuse to call in the painter to make it right. We don't even mind taking the car to be repaired after an accident—although here, human defensiveness usually rises up and makes us tell a story that frees us of any responsibility for the damage.

But how many of us really are alert to the signs of weathering and flaking on the surfaces of our marriages? How many of us try to slide out of facing the true facts of even a minor crash in our marriages? We simply find it impossible to admit that anything might be wrong with us or might be our fault, when actually admitting our fault need not be the shameful procedure that most people think it is. On the contrary, sometimes it can be like a cool, refreshing bath on a hot day which shakes one awake and gives one new strength.

Symptoms of an Ailing Marriage

What are some of the signs and symptoms of an ailing marriage? What might alert one or both partners in a marriage that all is not well with their partnership? First and foremost, I would put lack of communication between the partners.

There is a period in the very young child's life when he has not yet learned how to play with others. At that time you may see two two-year-olds playing in the same room or sandbox, each one completely unaware of the other, each one happily engrossed in his own play world. This is called by child specialists, "parallel play." Each two-year-old may be expected to continue his own happy and busy play activity without any awareness of the other, unless their physical paths happen to cross in the form of an actual collision or both want the same toy or tool. Then you may expect the screams to wax loud. At this period in their lives, no amount of quaint adult talk about "sharing" or "understanding the other fellow's needs" would make a bit of difference. The two are in a stage where only self-concern matters to each one of them. It is useless to try reaching their threshold of understanding with any other notion.

Some marriages are quite like "parallel play." Each partner pursues his life, his thoughts, his interests, quite unmindful of those of the other fellow's, unaware that they even exist. True, the partners meet on such occasions as mealtimes and bedtimes, but the meetings are incidental to their real interest, which is, of course, existing for themselves, each in his own orbit of activity.

The partners may believe that they communicate with each other. They tell each other about the things that have been happening to them in the office, in the home, on the street, with friends. But the really deep things that have been happening to them, the things about which they have strong feelings and anxieties—such as sex, failures, frustrations, evidences of unfriendliness from outsiders—these things the partners do not know how to communicate one to the other. Not knowing how to do this, the partners rarely if ever are called upon to give strength and comfort to each other.

Communication Between Man and Wife

This inability or unwillingness to communicate what is bothering them is labeled "unselfishness." "No," thinks the wife, "I have terrible fears in meeting strangers—anxieties that they won't like me. I know that Mrs. So-and-so didn't like me because when I met her in the supermarket today she said such-and-such to me, and I know this means that she not only doesn't like me but thinks I am a failure as a wife and mother. But even though this is eating me up, I must not talk about it to

Jim. It isn't right for a wife to load her problems on her husband. I must be the unselfish wife and keep these problems to myself."

Thinks the husband: "That job I have isn't getting me very far. Actually, I think I am pretty much of a failure in it. Look at So-and-so, who has already been promoted out of his department after only half the time on his job that I've been on mine. If only I'd taken those extra courses at college instead of playing football. I guess I'm pretty much of a lightweight and won't ever be much good in this world. But, of course, I mustn't tell Betty all this. It would be selfish to load any of this on her. A man is supposed to be the strong one and carry this kind of a load on his own shoulders."

Actually, how selfish these two are, not unselfish. There is an old-fashioned word that used to be used in marriage. A wife was called a "helpmeet," and actually, isn't that what wives, and husbands, too, are meant to be to each other—helpmeets? How selfish if they deny to their partners the opportunity to help each the other. Marriage is the one great opportunity we have outside of parenthood of being everything to another person, and of having that other person be everything to us. How can you-yourself take it upon yourself to deny your helpmeet the chance of truly helping *you?* If you give your partner this chance, you make it possible for him to grow, to try to meet your own deep needs and, by truly learning how to be your helpmeet, to become a bigger person and one far more capable of meeting life's challenges.

But this chance for your partner is impossible unless you-yourself learn the art of communication. And it *is* truly an art. Communicating as man and wife doesn't mean that the minute you get together you unload your petty cares and problems of the day—whether or not the washing machine works, whether the baby used twice as many diapers as he ordinarily does, whether the butcher gave you the wrong cut of meat. What do these things have to do with marriage? They are the wife's business only. It *is* selfish of her to load them onto her husband.

Whether or not the new stenographer is working out, whether the printing plant did or did not deliver those brochures in time, whether or not the new advertising campaign is going over—these are truly the husband's problems and it *is* selfish of him to bring them home and load them on to his wife.

Your Feelings That Count

But the deep feelings of adequacy or inadequacy in human relations, close or remote, the feelings of anger and anxiety, distrust and hate, of failure and frustration and despair—and also the great feelings of sweetness, happiness, success and exaltation—these are the feelings that do need to be shared with each other.

Little moments of communication need to be snatched from the stress and humdrum of living, perhaps over the dishes, perhaps while one is in the shower and one is shaving, perhaps at a party, perhaps in those last few moments of pillow-talk before going to sleep. These are golden moments of communication between two people that belong to them and to them alone in the world. These are the building blocks of a good marriage. Lack of them is one of the signs and symptoms of an ailing marriage.

Next time you are at a party notice which husbands and wives have something to say to each other during the course of an evening, and which do not. I have been astounded to see couples who, from the beginning of the evening to the very end, are apparently unaware that the other is in the room. How extraordinary this is, and how different from their courting and early marriage days when it was difficult for either one of them to notice anyone else in the room! Now it is just the opposite.

When I see this in couples, my heart is sad for them and for what they have lost. For they have lost that electric awareness of each other, that sense that each is the most exciting person in the world for the other, the most stimulating, the most dear, and the one above all with whom each wants to share everything. They have lost that all-consuming urge to be part of each other. This being so, neither knows how to be a true helpmeet to the other.

When There Is Only Sex

I have dwelt on the lack of communication between partners as the most significant element in poor marital adjustment because of the queer thing that happens to sexual relations in such marriages. I mentioned that husbands and wives who have not developed the art of communicating with each other lead parallel but not interlocking lives, meeting at meals, in social gatherings and in bed. Such marriages probably are held together almost purely by the sexual relationship, provided that it is a satisfactory one to both people. If it is not, then the total relationship falls to pieces and the marriage probably will break up. But in cases where the sexual relationship *is* satisfying, let's examine the overall relationship a little more closely.

Let's say that two people have in common the external trappings of marriage—that is, a home, a social life, children and the one bond of a sexual relationship which the two partners would call satisfying. By this they mean that the frequency of sex is mutually agreeable and that both partners have what they consider adequate sexual release. There is no question but that such a marriage, cemented as it is by the one common fact of sex and ordinary social intercourse, can continue—under ordinary circumstances. This is the kind of marriage, however, that very often does not survive stress. I refer to such stress, for instance, as the sudden discovery by one of the partners that the man-woman relationship can mean far more than just meeting in bed.

Because of the possibility of such a discovery it becomes important to examine just what the sexual relationship really does mean to two people who haven't discovered the art of communicating with each other.

It means (a) agreeable sexual satisfaction, (b) this becomes the sole satisfactory point of contact between the two partners, (c) it does not involve anyone else (servants, friends or children). These are very positive points in its favor.

What Sex Alone Does Not Achieve

What does sexual intercourse in this type of marriage *not* stand for? It does *not* stand for (a) a means of communication between the partners, (b) an expression of the growing love between the partners, (c) a symbol of the deepening total relationship between the husband and the wife.

Thus, the chances of the sexual relation in such a marriage ever representing any more than exactly that, a sexual relationship, are not too bright. And I think this would be the moment to indicate that rarely, if ever, is sex *as sex* completely satisfying. When you've had it, what have you had? Answer—sex. And is sex *the* great answer in life? If it were, then in any world, especially our own modern world, you wouldn't have to marry in order to have it. Let's be brutal and face the fact that sex as sex is easily obtained as a commercial transaction, with payment not always made in cold currency.

By now you may have gotten some inkling as to why I have spent so much time on two subjects—communication between two partners and the actual significance to the partners of sex in their marriage.

Use and Misuse of Your Partner

Another symptom of an ailing marriage is the use that one partner may be making of the other within the marriage. Is one person using his or her partner to further his own ends, to bolster his insecure ego, thus hoping to fortify shaky relationships? Or even, most tragically, to serve as the very handy and ever-present target of revenge and cruelty, a kind of captive victim through whose helplessness a frustrated and angry human being can vent his vengefulness and spleen on the world? This use—or perhaps I should say misuse or abuse—usually extends not only to the partner, but to the equally helpless and captive children.

The home in which you observe this situation obviously is not a real home, but a place of torment and fear, crippling to those who are held subject in it. Contrasted with the home where there is no communication between husband and wife, in this home the communication is all too present, but it has only one direction—from the hater to the hated, with sex often the most violent of the weapons used.

This kind of sickness in marriage can run the gamut of seriousness from very slight to almost fatal. It is possible for a couple to catch the symptoms and the illness early, in a less serious stage, and take their marriage to a source of help. This must be done, however, with honest good will and good intent on both sides. As I have stated, it takes two to make a marriage but only one to wreck it.

Seeking Outside Help

To whom to go if the two of you are not able to handle the situation yourselves?

In the last ten or fifteen years there has developed a new professional group called marriage counselors. Numerically, they are not a very large group and, unfortunately, they are mostly found only in the fairly big cities. Professionally, the background of these people may be medicine (including psychiatry), the ministry or psychology. Several centers in the United States offer training in marriage counseling, and the professional group to which a properly accredited marriage counselor belongs is called the American Association of Marriage Counselors.

Some theological seminaries have inaugurated training in pastoral counseling for their students, a part of which includes marriage counseling. It is encouraging to note the current increased interest in marriage counseling in all religious groups, Protestant, Jewish and Catholic. To be an accredited marriage counselor, however, a clergyman would, in addition, have to take a full course of training at one of the accredited centers in order to entitle him to this professional designation.

Certain counselors associated with family courts such as those in Toledo, Detroit, New York and elsewhere, offer valuable services which couples applying for divorce are encouraged to use. It is a pity, however, that so many couples wait until the desperate measure of divorce is undertaken before seeking help. By the time a marriage has reached this point, many cruel, bitter, ugly and unforgettable things have been said and done on both sides. It is like an ugly burn in a piece of beautiful tapestry. Skilled fingers may be able to repair it in such a way that the injury may not be visible to the outsider, but *you* always know it is there. How much better it would have been had the damage never occurred in the first place.

If the trained marriage counselor is not available, the help that *is* available should be sought and used. Your minister, your doctor, a wise family lawyer, a court judge in his off hours, a social service worker—all may lend a helping hand. What is to hinder you, if you are really deeply concerned about your marriage, from seeking help where help may be found? Often all that may be needed in the early stages of difficulty is the counsel of a wise and kind person. He can help two people face themselves as they are, so that they themselves may realize that what they already have in the marriage is worth building on.

All too often people dash off and get a divorce at the drop of a hat, simply when things become uncomfortable or fail to work out as they would like. They fool themselves into believing that the next marriage will be wonderful. After they have gone through the artificial excitement of another honeymoon, what do they usually find? Just about what they found in the first marriage. Changing mates hasn't changed their problems.

The Investment You Make in Marriage

Marriage isn't like tennis where you team up with a partner for an afternoon's pleasant game. Marriage is really a form of emotional banking. It is a deep and heavy investment by two people. They put a great sum into their marriage, which is irretrievably lost by divorce. In business, when you invest you have to protect your investment. You protect it in several ways—by a great deal of hard work and effort, by integrity, and *by additional investment.*

To protect a good investment, many businessmen feel that no effort is too great. What is wrong, then, with protecting your marriage as an emotional investment? Why kick your marriage around—or why kick your partner in marriage around? Why not invest a little more and salvage your original investment?

There is no question but that some separations and divorces are necessary, but in the minds of many sober people, an equal number of broken marriages are wasteful. They result only in swapping partners and beginning the same old dance with a new partner. The people involved arrive at age forty-five or fifty in emotional bankruptcy. They have put very little of themselves into marriage. Whatever they have done has been more or less for selfish motives which they have not been willing to sacrifice for the sake of their marriage. Thus it is that they approach the end of their lives with empty hearths, empty hands, and empty hearts.

Pity them—and learn from them.

19

Moment of Truth

What can yet be said?

Basic to the stability of the world is the enduring man-woman relationship. The Committee on the Family in Contemporary Society of the 1958 Lambeth Conference of Anglican (Episcopal) Bishops set forth one of the three great and equally important purposes of marriage in these luminous words: ". . . The need of man and woman for each other, to complement and fulfill each other and to establish a durable partnership against the loneliness and rigor of life."

The loneliness and rigor of life—there it is. This is what motivates our eternal need for shelter and comfort in another human being: *the loneliness and rigor of life.* Bright lights can not dispel its darkness, jukeboxes can not banish its awful silence, crowds can not fill its emptiness, marble and stainless steel can not build a refuge from it. For most of us only one thing can accomplish all of these: that durable partnership of a man and a woman who live together with the mutual gift of devotion.

Marriage can shackle you or marriage can free you—depending on how you look at it and how you feel about it. And make no mistake—you two, and only you two, will decide the fate of your marriage.

There comes in every marriage that one single moment—the moment of truth—when you take a decision for your marriage, or against it.

That decision will be final. If it is against, nothing anyone else can do will save the marriage. But if it is for . . .

Then you will find yourselves able to do anything, be anything, suffer anything, for the sake of it. *Then* you will truly have committed yourselves to your marriage.

Early in the book, I told the story of the priest who, when I was a child, had me guessing as to what was the most beautiful age in life.

Here, I could paraphrase his question: What is the most beautiful love? And his answer: The love you have, my child, the love you have.

Cherish that love, that it may always remain beautiful—and your own.

Suggested Reading

Your First Week Together, by William and Alice Brown. National Council of Churches.

Sexual Harmony in Marriage, by Oliver M. Butterfield, Ph.D. Emerson Books, Inc.

Facts of Life for Children, by the Staff of the Child Study Association of America. Maco Books, Inc.

Facts of Life and Love for Teenagers, by Evelyn Millis Duvall. Association Press.

When You Marry, by Evelyn Duvall and Reuben Hill. D. C. Heath.

Expectant Motherhood, by Nicholson J. Eastman, M.D. Little, Brown & Co.

Husbands and Pregnancy, by The Reverend William Genné. Association Press.

A Doctor's Marital Guide for Patients, by Bernard R. Greenblatt, M.D. Planned Parenthood Federation of America.

Having a Baby, by Alan F. Guttmacher, M.D. Pocket Books.

The Catholic Marriage Manual, by The Reverend George A. Kelly. Random House, Inc.

Youth Looks Toward Marriage, by David R. Mace. Darwen Finlayson, Ltd., London, England.

Whom God Hath Joined, by David R. Mace. Westminster Press.

To Those Denied a Child, Planned Parenthood.

Happiness in Marriage, by Margaret Sanger. Coward-McCann, Inc.

A Marriage Manual, by Hannah Stone, M.D., and Abraham Stone, M.D. Simon and Schuster, Inc.

Prevention of Conception, by Abraham Stone, M.D. Planned Parenthood.

Love Is Not What You Think, by Jessamyn West. Harcourt, Brace & Co.

If I Marry a Roman Catholic, by The Reverend Leland F. Wood. National Council of Churches.

ABOUT THE AUTHOR

Dr. Mary Steichen Calderone is a graduate of Brearley School, Vassar College, the University of Rochester Medical School and Columbia University School of Public Health. After serving her internship in the Children's Medical Service of Bellevue Hospital, she was awarded a two-year fellowship by New York City's Department of Health. Her first position after receiving her degree in Public Health was with the then newly established Merit System Study of the American Public Health Association, where she set up the first pool of examination questions for health officers.

Dr. Calderone has long been active in her own community, Great Neck, Long Island, where she served for several years as a school physician. She has been on the board of the Mental Health Association of Nassau County, which in 1956 bestowed on her a citation for public service, and has talked on mental health and sex education before parent-teacher groups throughout the area. Since October, 1953, she has been Medical Director of the Planned Parenthood Federation of America. A Fellow of the American Public Health Association, she is a member of the American Society for the Study of Sterility, the International Fertility Association, and the Society for the Scientific Study of Sex.

Dr. Calderone is a Quaker. She is the wife of Dr. Frank A. Calderone, former Deputy Commissioner of Health of New York City, who has served with the World Health Organization and as Director of Health Services for the United Nations Secretariat. They have three daughters, two of whom are still in school, and two grandsons. Dr. Calderone's interests include house plants, cooking, and blue-water sailing in the West Indies with her husband on their schooner *Tradition.*

Phyllis and Robert Goldman are science writers who specialize in medical subjects. Mr. Goldman holds five awards in the field of science writing and has, for the past nine years, been associate editor of *Parade,* a syndicated Sunday magazine appearing in newspapers throughout the United States. The Goldmans have one child, a son.